Challenging puzzles *for* word fanatics

GEORGE BREDEHORN

Official Mensa Puzzle Book

Sterling Publishing Co., Inc.
New York

Edited and designed by Peter Gordon

10 9 8 7 6 5 4 3 2 1

Published by Sterling Publishing Company, Inc.
387 Park Avenue South, New York, N.Y. 10016

Distributed in Canada by Sterling Publishing
c/o Canadian Manda Group, 165 Dufferin Street
Toronto, Ontario, Canada M6K 3H6
Distributed in the United Kingdom by GMC Distribution Services,
Castle Place, 166 High Street, Lewes, East Sussex, England BN7 1XU
Distributed in Australia by Capricorn Link (Australia) Pty Ltd.
P.O. Box 704, Windsor, NSW 2756, Australia

Manufactured in China

Sterling ISBN-13: 978-1-4027-4307-8
ISBN-10: 1-4027-4307-6

For information about custom editions, special sales, premium and
corporate purchases, please contact Sterling Special Sales
Department at 800-805-5489 or specialsales@sterlingpub.com.

CONTENTS

INTRODUCTION

I have loads of friends who are expert solvers, constructors, and editors of crossword puzzles. If there's anything that I'm worse at than constructing crosswords, it's solving them. However, I consider myself a crackerjack inventor of different types of word puzzles! It's fun, risky, and certainly creative. Why is it fun? I'm coming up with something that may never have been done before. Inventing is a kind of adventurous fun. Why is it risky? On Saturday, I may have the germ of a puzzle idea. On Sunday, Monday, and Tuesday I'll develop and fine-tune my creation. On Wednesday, I'll look at my masterpiece and suddenly realize that it's boring and too difficult and complicated to pursue. "How did I come up with this piece of garbage?" I think. But on the other side of the coin is the ego boost that results when a creative effort is accepted by an editor of a newspaper or book. There's a world of difference between being creative and being creative and getting paid for it.

This book has more than 100 puzzles, made up of 10 different puzzle types. You may have seen Split Decisions and Two by Two puzzles in a magazine or newspaper. The other types are less well-known, but no less enjoyable. Solve them in order, or jump around, but be sure to have fun!

—George Bredehorn

DIRECTIONS

CLUELESS CROSSWORDS

Fill in the blanks in the grid so that eight seven-letter words are formed.

DOUBLE EXPOSURE

First, figure out the six-letter words that read from top to bottom in the columns. Half of the letters are already revealed. Then take one letter from the top three squares of each column and transfer it to the blank above to reveal a phrase. Lines divide words. A second phrase is similarly formed on the bottom from the bottom three letters in each column.

FILL-IN STATION

Fill in the grid with the nine letters given on the right so that three-letter words are formed in all the directions that the arrows point.

THE FINAL WORD

Unscramble the four-letter word at the top. Transfer the letter over the numbered blank to the same numbered blanks to the left of the plus signs. Continue in this fashion until you get the final word, which completes the quote. Some words may have more than one anagram, but there's only one way to get to the correct final word.

FRAZE-IT

Fill in the two defined words in each line. Keeping the letter sequence, transfer the boxed letters to the blanks below, where the phrase will appear.

LATTICEWORK

Fill in the blanks so that the words interlock and fit the given category. Spaces are ignored when entering letters.

MIXAGRAMS

Each line contains a five-letter word and a four-letter word whose letters have been mixed, but the left-to-right order of the letters has not been changed. Unmix the two words on each line and write them in the spaces provided. When you're done, the answer to the clue will appear reading down in the two marked columns.

Example: D A R I U N V E T = DRIVE + AUNT

SPLIT DECISIONS

The only clues in this puzzle are the letter pairs given in the grid. Each answer consists of a pair of words that share the letters that are to be entered in the empty squares. In the example, we've filled in the letters S, I, and D to make the words SOLID and SQUID. No proper names or hyphenated words are used. A few of the combinations may have more than one possible solution, but only one will work with all the crossings.

Example: [ ] [O/Q] [L/U] [ ] [ ] becomes [S] [O/Q] [L/U] [I] [D]

TRIAD SPLIT DECISIONS

This puzzle is just like Split Decisions, except that three letters are given for each word instead of two. In the example, we've filled in the letters C, A, and L to make the words CEREAL and CASUAL.

Example: [ ] [E/A] [R/S] [E/U] [ ] [ ] becomes [C] [E/A] [R/S] [E/U] [A] [L]

TWO BY TWO

Only two different letters are needed to complete each of these miniature crisscross puzzles. All the vowels have been placed for you. Pick two consonants and repeat them as often as necessary to finish each grid. No words are repeated in any one puzzle, and no proper names, hyphenated words, or words containing apostrophes are used.

CLUELESS CROSSWORDS

Directions, page 6

Answer, page 78

				D		D
E						E
G				V		S
U		P				
		G	J			
				T		
R			R			

	E			A		
W		L				
	I					N
						K
M		G				A
				G		
D	E	S				D

SPLIT DECISIONS

Directions, page 7 *Answer, page 83*

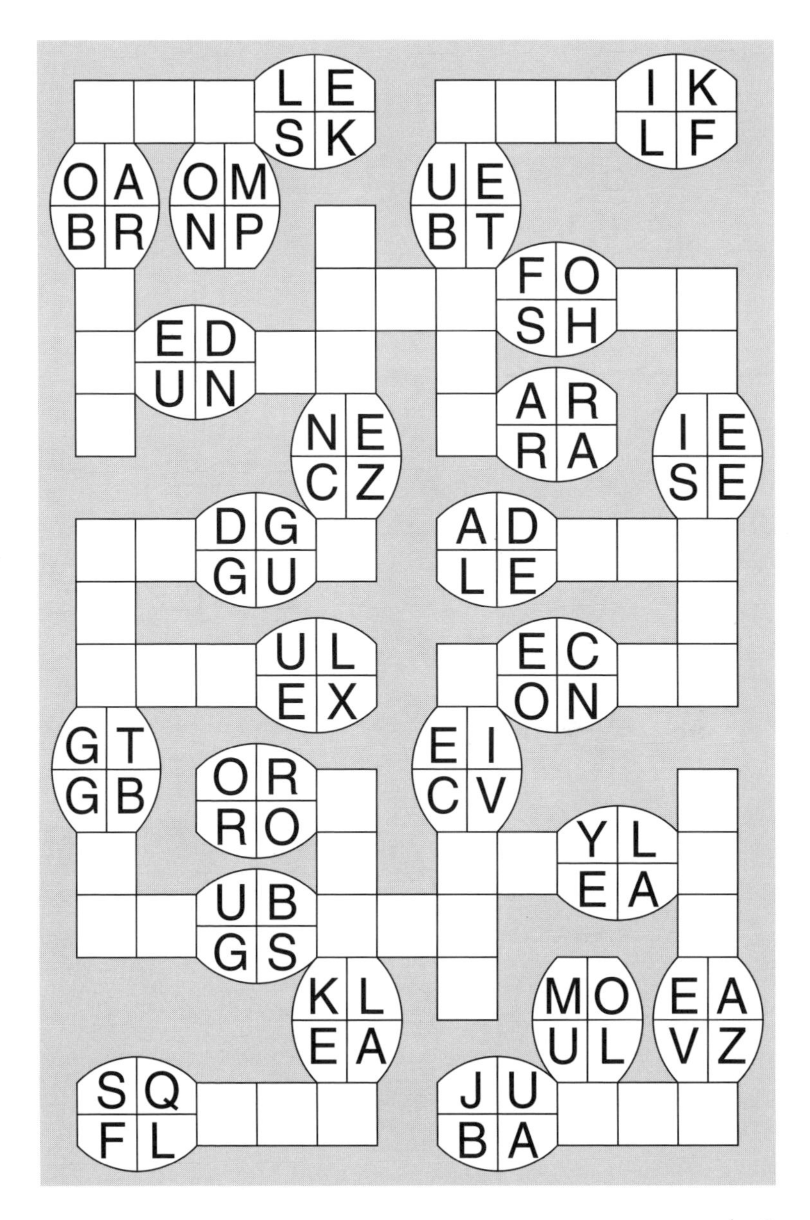

TWO BY TWO

Directions, page 7

Answer, page 92

TRIAD SPLIT DECISIONS

Directions, page 7

Answer, page 75

SPLIT DECISIONS

Directions, page 7 *Answer, page 91*

MIXAGRAMS

Directions, page 7 *Answer, page 90*

1 Clue: It's good to unwind in the wind

KLOITCOTY = _ _ _ _ _ + _ _ _ _

RITOCHOFY = _ _ _ _ _ + _ _ _ _

THEROPICO = _ _ _ _ _ + _ _ _ _

LEANSUDEY = _ _ _ _ _ + _ _ _ _

2 Clue: At least one is needed to shoulder general responsibility

BIGROBSAN = _ _ _ _ _ + _ _ _ _

OCBOCOURT = _ _ _ _ _ + _ _ _ _

SLIMODITA = _ _ _ _ _ + _ _ _ _

DEDONURSE = _ _ _ _ _ + _ _ _ _

FRAZE-IT

Directions, page 6 *Answer, page 86*

1 □ _ □ _ □ _ Cow's activity — □ _ _ □ Leg part

2 _ □ _ □ _ _ _ Pupil's place — _ □ _ □ _ Hospital worker

3 □ _ □ _ _ □ Pay no attention to — □ _ _ □ _ Melting snow

Phrase: _ _ _ _ _ _ (1 1 1 1 1 2) _ _ _ _ _ _ _ _ (2 2 2 3 3 3 3 3)

1 □ _ □ _ □ Deep moan — □ _ _ _ □ Arm part

2 _ □ _ _ □ Stop by — □ _ □ _ □ Emerge from an egg

3 _ □ _ □ Cat's sound — _ □ _ □ _ □ Behaved badly

Phrase: _ _ _ _ (1 1 1 1) _ _ _ _ (1 2 2 2) _ _ _ (2 2 3) _ _ _ _ (3 3 3 3)

SPLIT DECISIONS

Directions, page 7 *Answer, page 75*

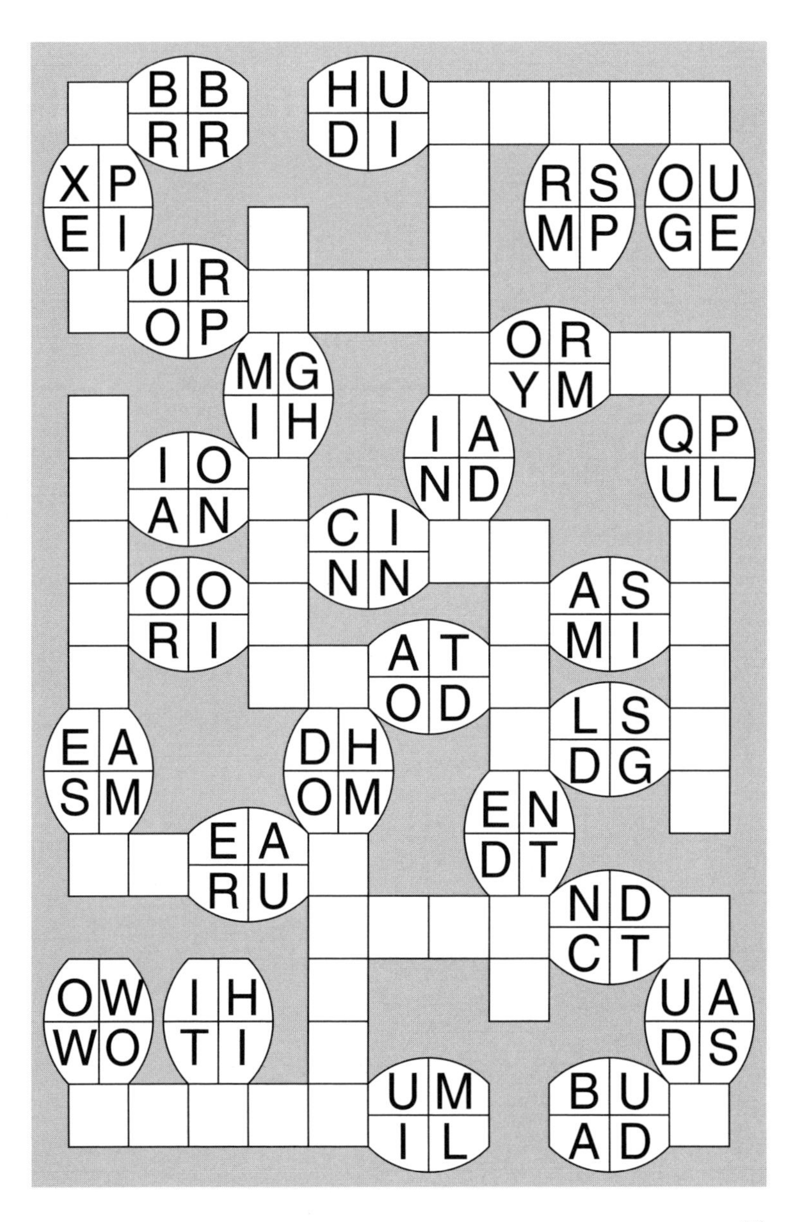

TRIAD SPLIT DECISIONS

Directions, page 7

Answer, page 77

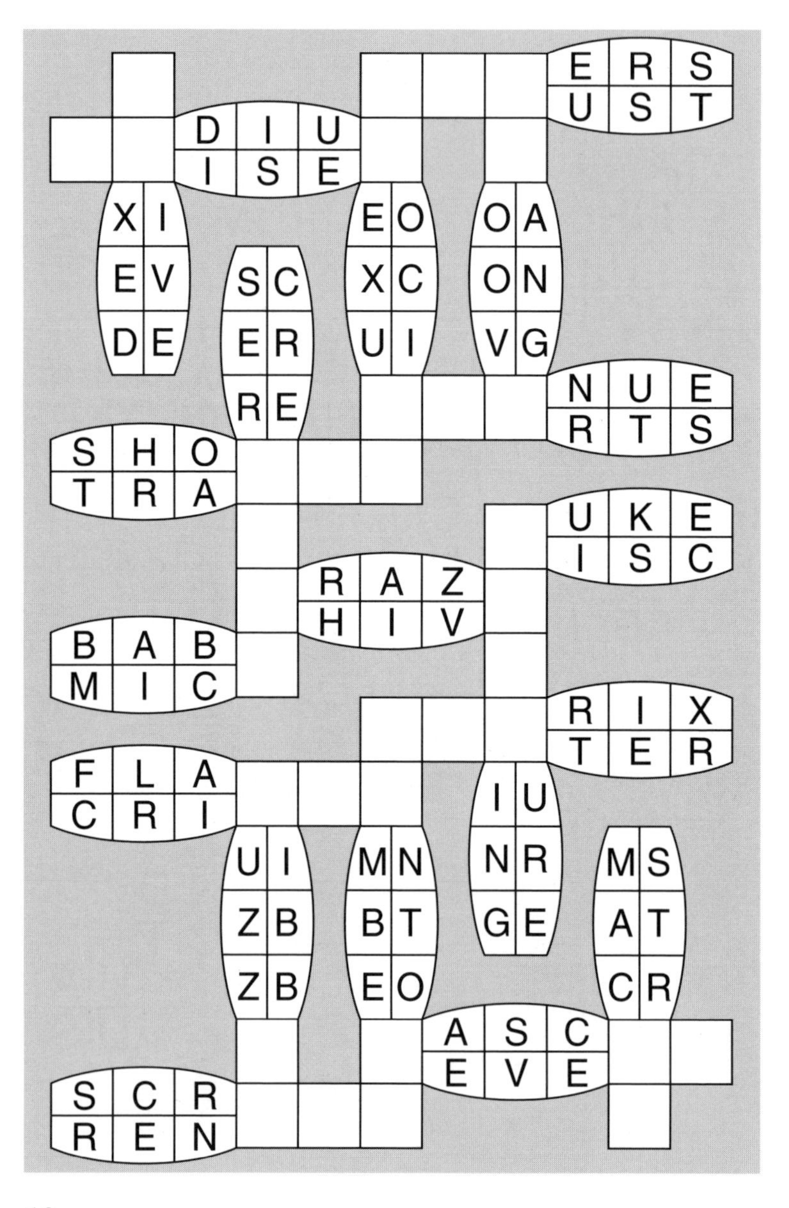

TWO BY TWO

Directions, page 7 *Answer, page 90*

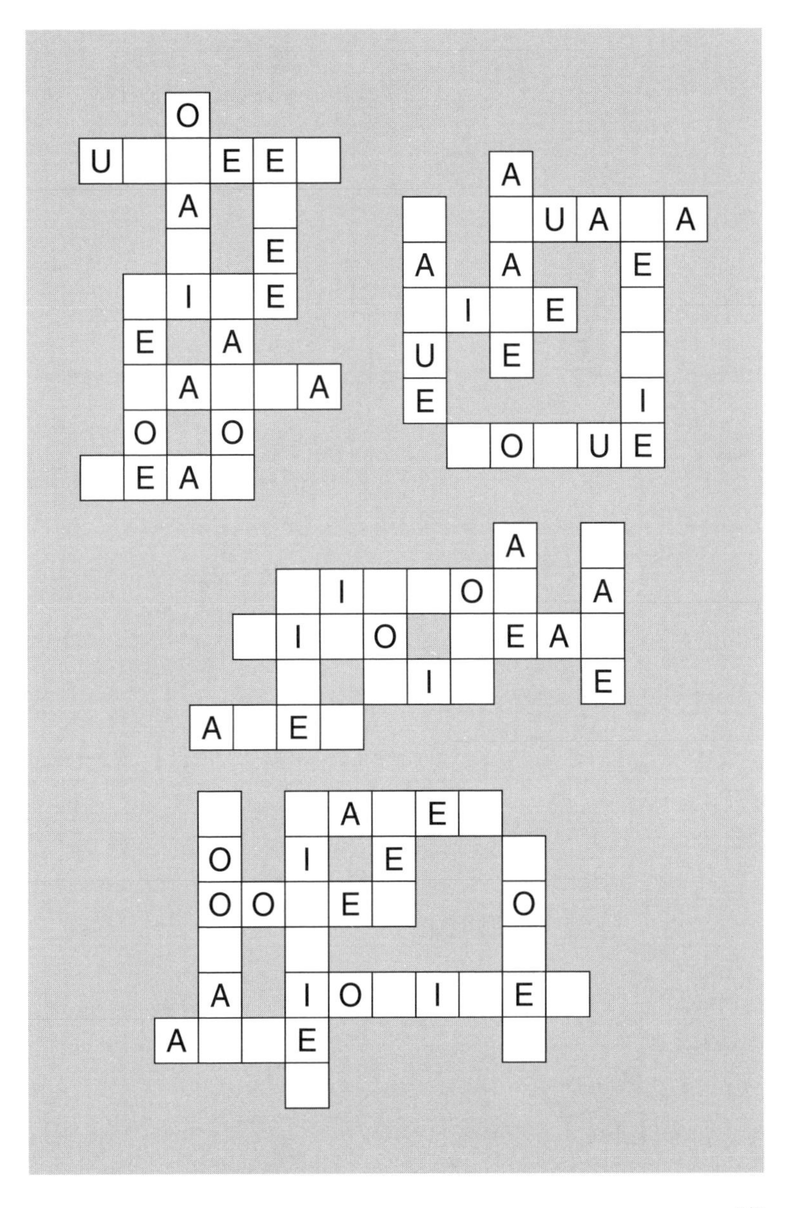

SPLIT DECISIONS

Directions, page 7 *Answer, page 73*

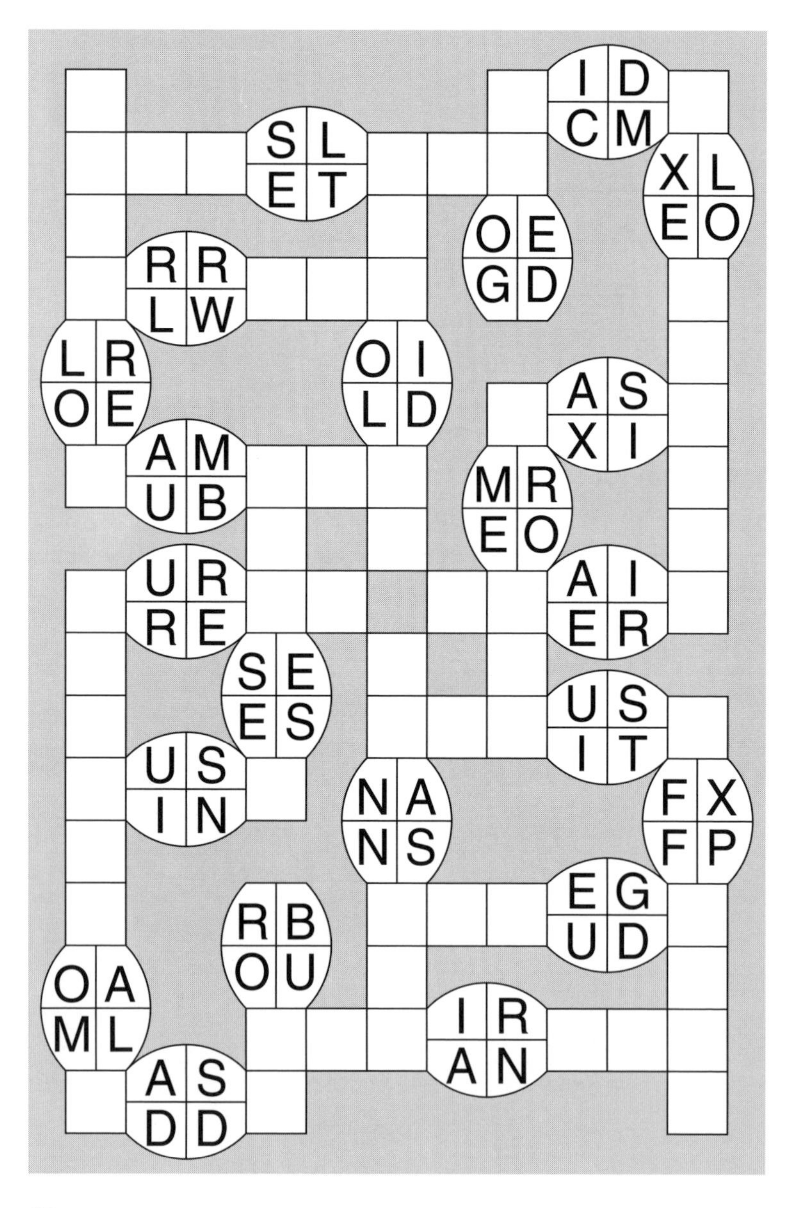

DOUBLE EXPOSURE

Directions, page 6

Answer, page 74

1

_ _ _ _ _ _ | _ _ _ _ _ _ _ _

	W		W	T			N		G				E
	R	E			W	E	O		R	W	L	E	
R		X		D		O		X		O		I	P
K	I		O				Z	I		F	A		R
			P		F	L			H		K		
T		R		M	S			D				O	

_ _ _ | _ _ _ _ _ _ | _ _ _ _ _

2

_ _ _ _ _ | _ _ _ | _ _ _ _ _ _

	W		A	V						K	C	J	
P	H	P	I		P		N	H		H		I	C
H				N	T			W	G		I		
		W	W		U	I			N		Q	N	
	C	N		M		E	K			I			S
X						K	Y	T	G				M

_ _ _ | _ _ _ _ | _ _ _ _ _ _ _

THE FINAL WORD

Directions, page 6 *Answer, page 82*

1

P E L K = _ _ _ _[1]

_[1] + P I O H = _ _ _ _ _[2]

_[1] _[2] + H E R G = _ _ _ _ _ _[3]

_[1] _[2] _[3] + S E P S = _ _ _ _ _ _ _[4]

_[1] _[2] _[3] _[4] + H E P Y = _ _ _ _ _ _ _ _

The Final Word

"It is the responsibility of the poet to be lazy, to hang out, and ___."

—Grace Paley

2

N O U D = _ _ _ _[1]

_[1] + T U N C = _ _ _ _ _[2]

_[1] _[2] + C O R D = _ _ _ _ _ _[3]

_[1] _[2] _[3] + E N N U = _ _ _ _ _ _ _[4]

_[1] _[2] _[3] _[4] + D I C E = _ _ _ _ _ _ _ _

The Final Word

"Example moves the world more than ___."

—Henry Miller

SPLIT DECISIONS

Directions, page 7 *Answer, page 92*

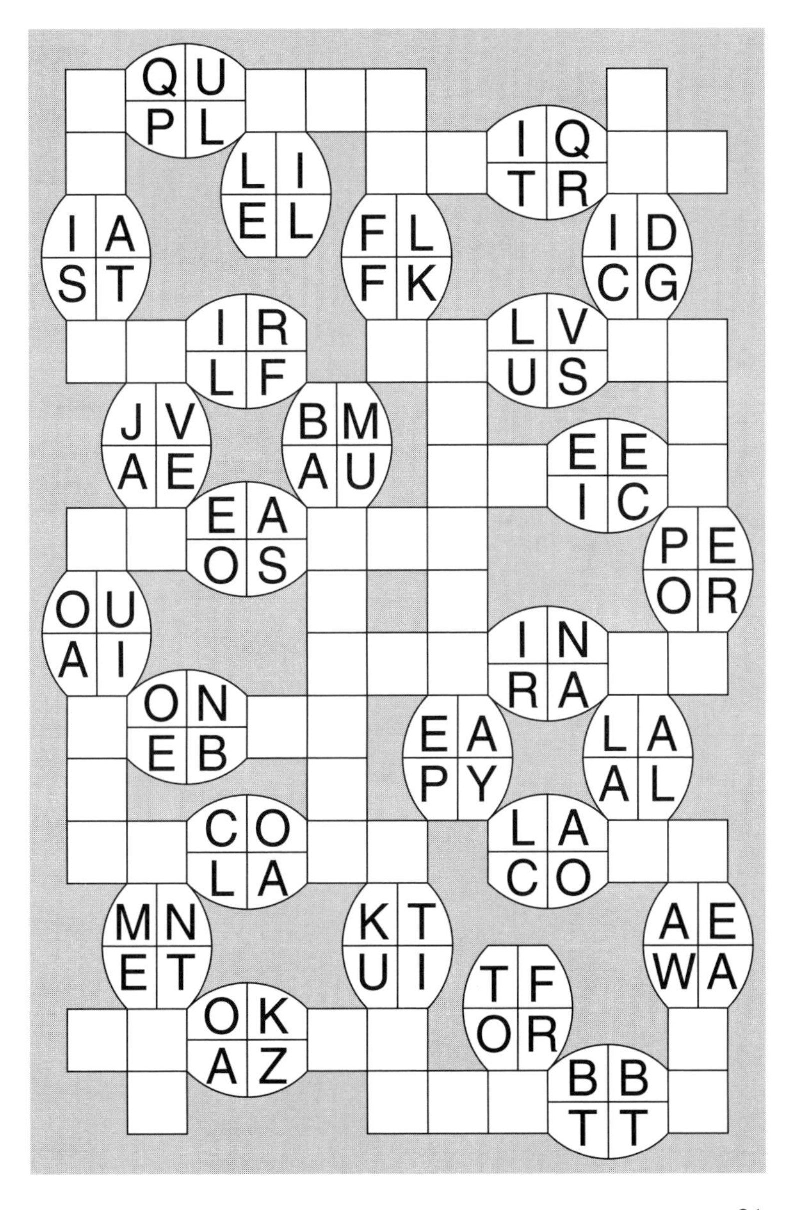

TRIAD SPLIT DECISIONS

Directions, page 7 *Answer, page 85*

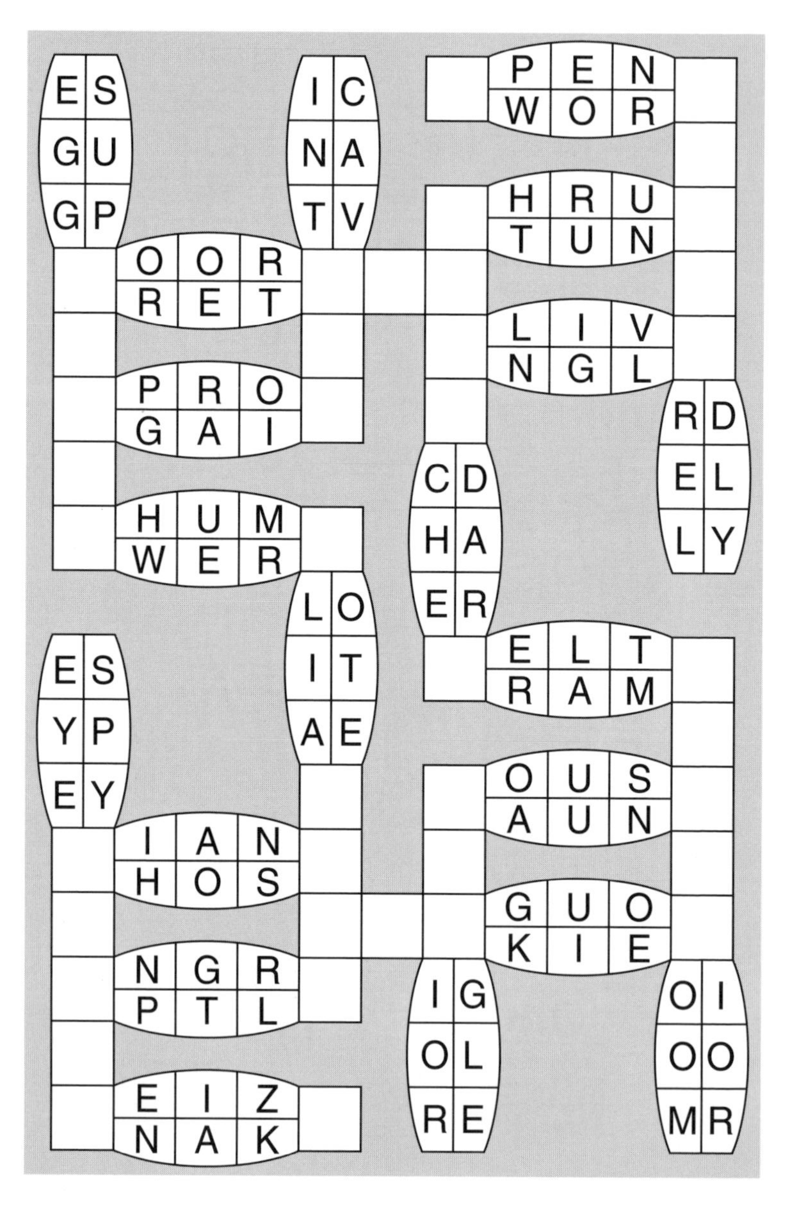

FRAZE-IT

Directions, page 6 *Answer, page 90*

1 _ _ ☐ _ ☐ _ ☐ Caught with a rope _ ☐ _ ☐ _ Less

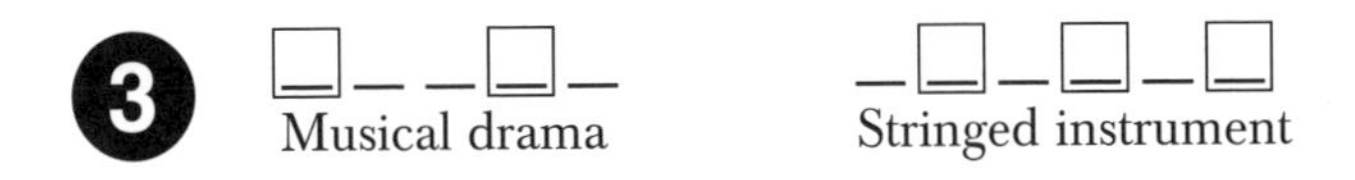

Phrase: _ _ _ _ _ _ (1 1 1 1 1 2) _ _ _ _ _ _ _ _ (2 2 2 3 3 3 3 3)

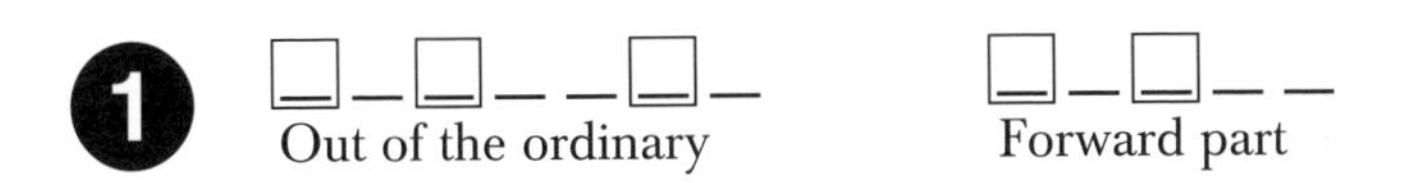

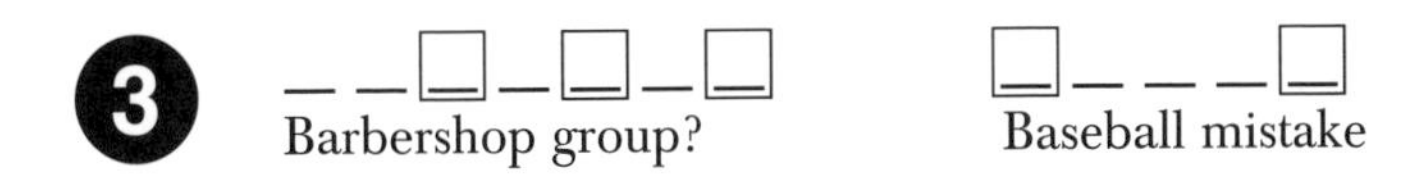

Phrase: _ _ _ _ _ _ _ (1 1 1 1 1 2 2) _ _ _ _ _ _ _ (2 2 3 3 3 3 3)

SPLIT DECISIONS

Directions, page 7 *Answer, page 77*

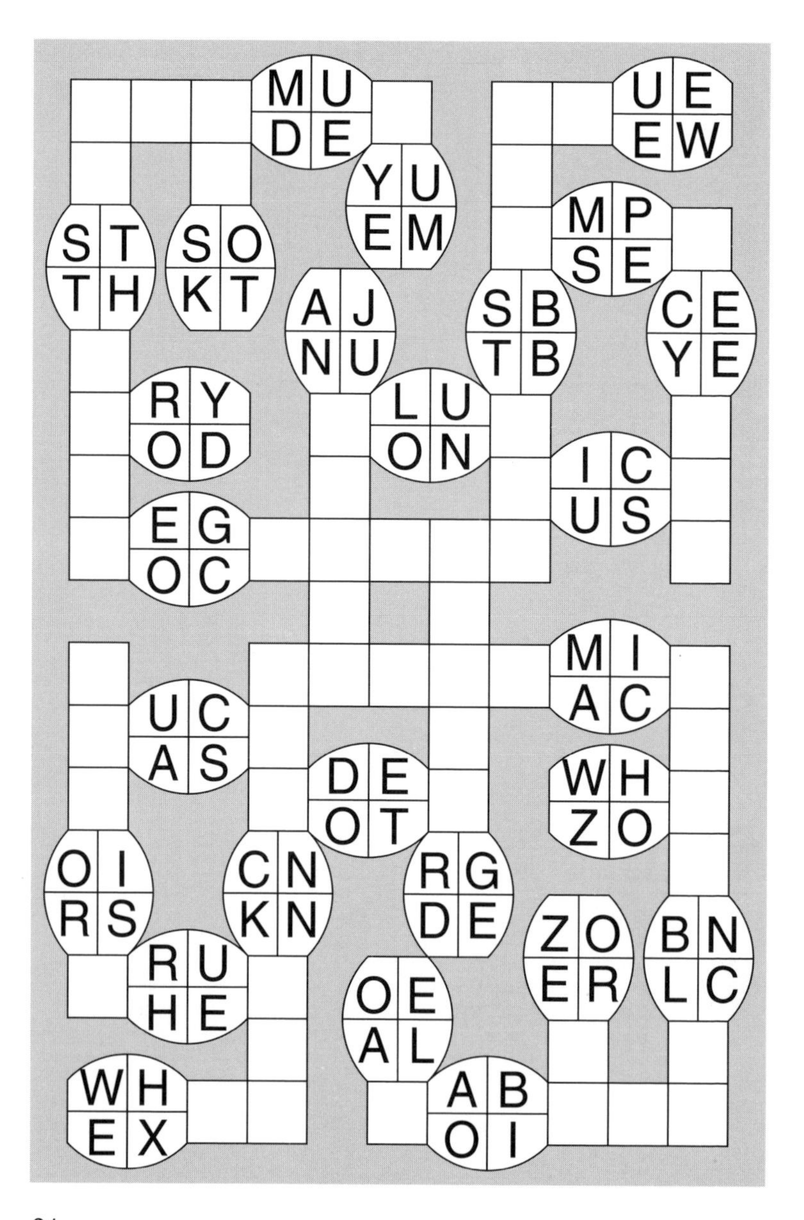

TWO BY TWO

Directions, page 7

Answer, page 79

TRIAD SPLIT DECISIONS

Directions, page 7

Answer, page 83

SPLIT DECISIONS

Directions, page 7

Answer, page 89

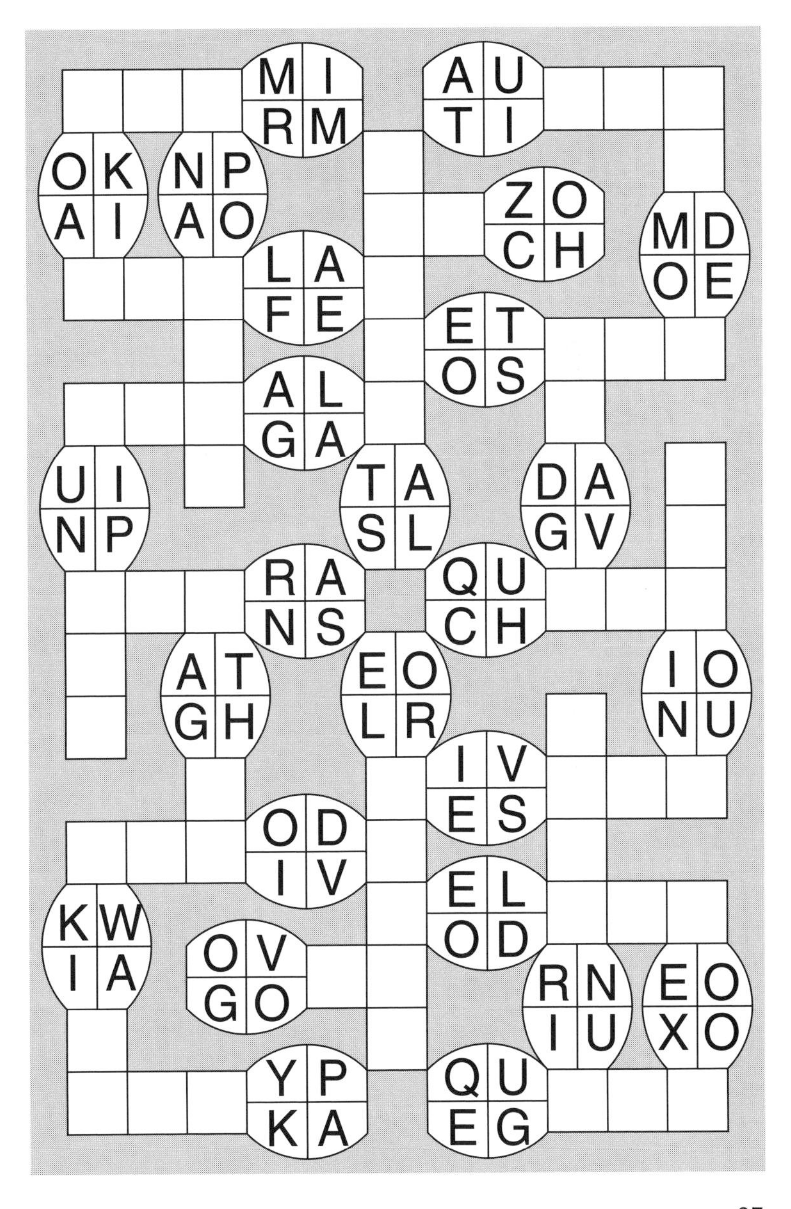

MIXAGRAMS

Directions, page 7 *Answer, page 79*

1

Clue: Where guys do a lot of standing around

↓ ↓

CAERRGOOM = _ _ _ _ _ _ + _ _ _ _

DOVEOGURE = _ _ _ _ _ _ + _ _ _ _

CRABOTINS = _ _ _ _ _ _ + _ _ _ _

SIAMNIDUS = _ _ _ _ _ _ + _ _ _ _

2

Clue: A key can't open this

↓ ↓

GULGLCHUM = _ _ _ _ _ _ + _ _ _ _

VODORIMCE = _ _ _ _ _ _ + _ _ _ _

SMOCCUHAM = _ _ _ _ _ _ + _ _ _ _

SHAKARIND = _ _ _ _ _ _ + _ _ _ _

SPLIT DECISIONS

Directions, page 7

Answer, page 81

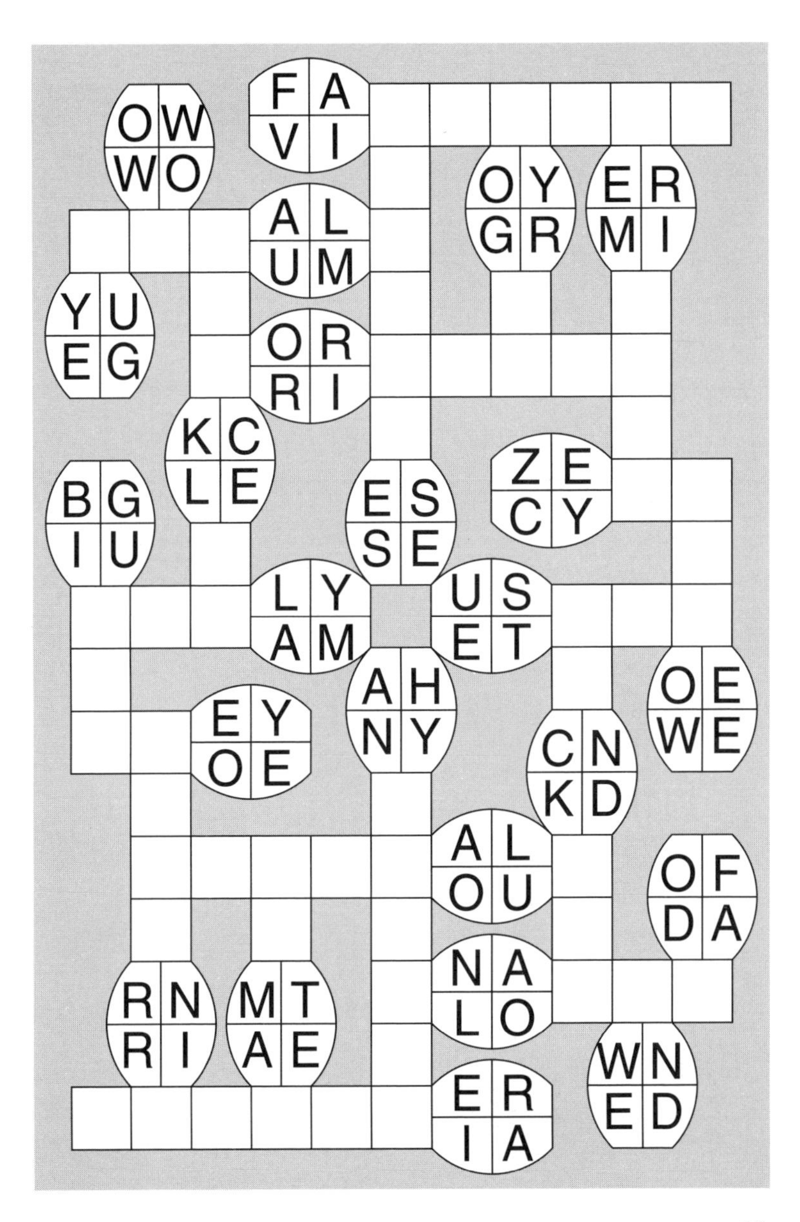

TRIAD SPLIT DECISIONS

Directions, page 7 *Answer, page 85*

LATTICEWORK

Directions, page 6

Answer, page 80

SPLIT DECISIONS

Directions, page 7

Answer, page 75

TWO BY TWO

Directions, page 7

Answer, page 78

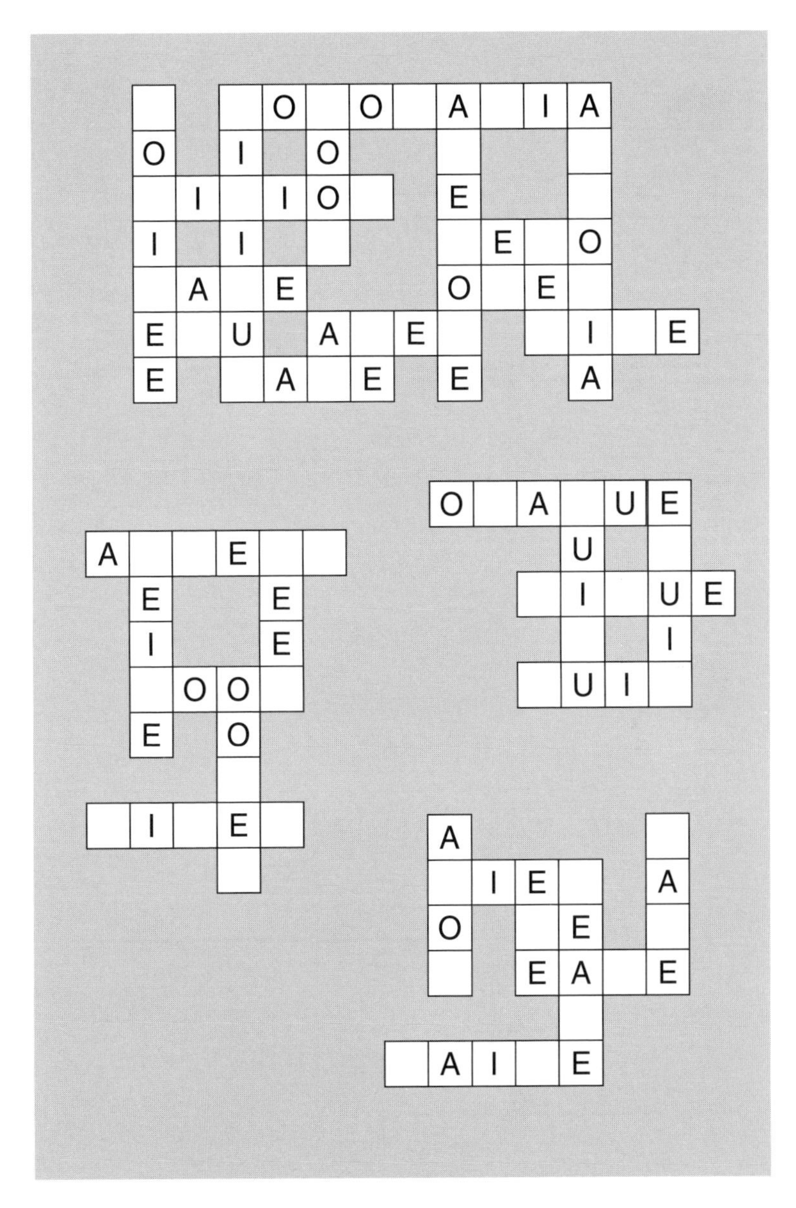

DOUBLE EXPOSURE

Directions, page 6 *Answer, page 80*

1

V	A				J		M	E	L	J	M	S	
O	W	X		R								W	R
				U	K	T		P	Z				U
			R	A	E	S		L		G	E		
V	L	A	V				U		L			V	
		S	Y			P	K			N	P		M

2

J	B	N		Z			S	J				P	C
				I		Y	U		R	S	K		Y
	X				B			D	M	Y	I	C	
K			V	H	U	V	O				E		
		E	O										C
L	G	I	Y		T	N		D	L	O		P	

SPLIT DECISIONS

Directions, page 7

Answer, page 85

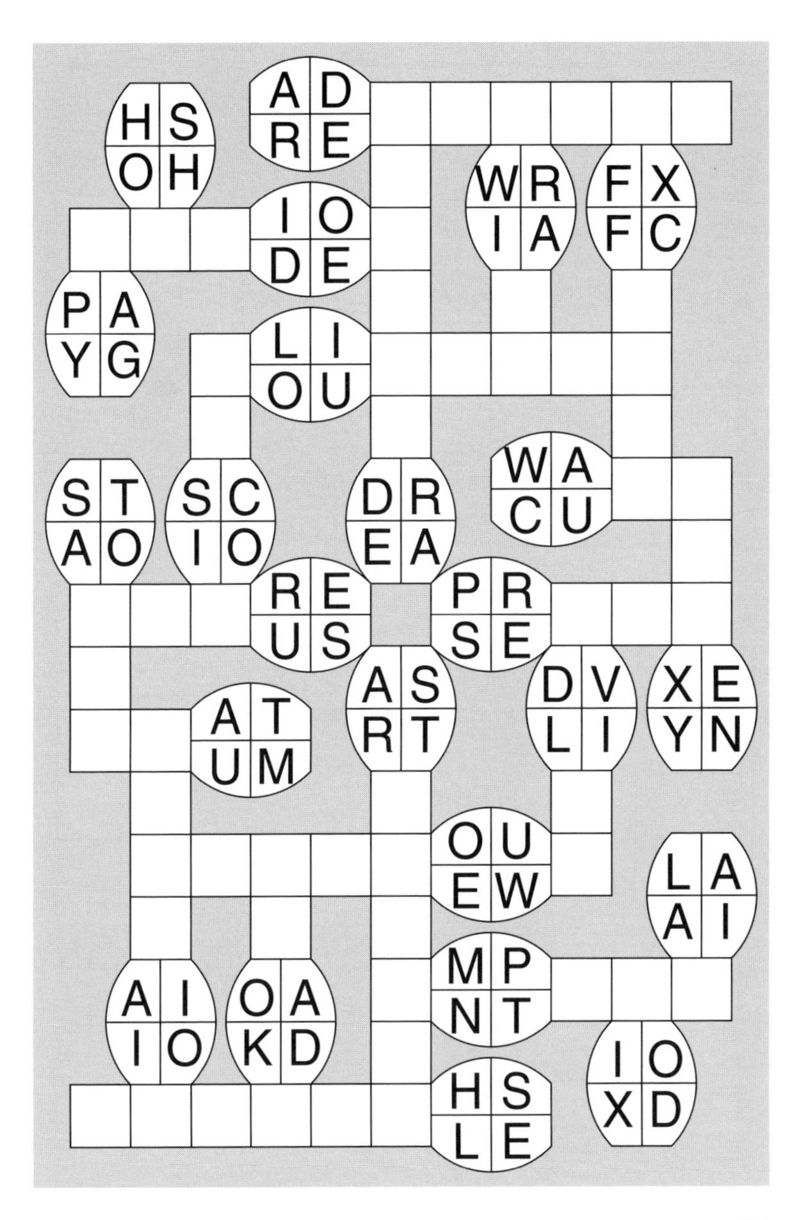

TRIAD SPLIT DECISIONS

Directions, page 7

Answer, page 89

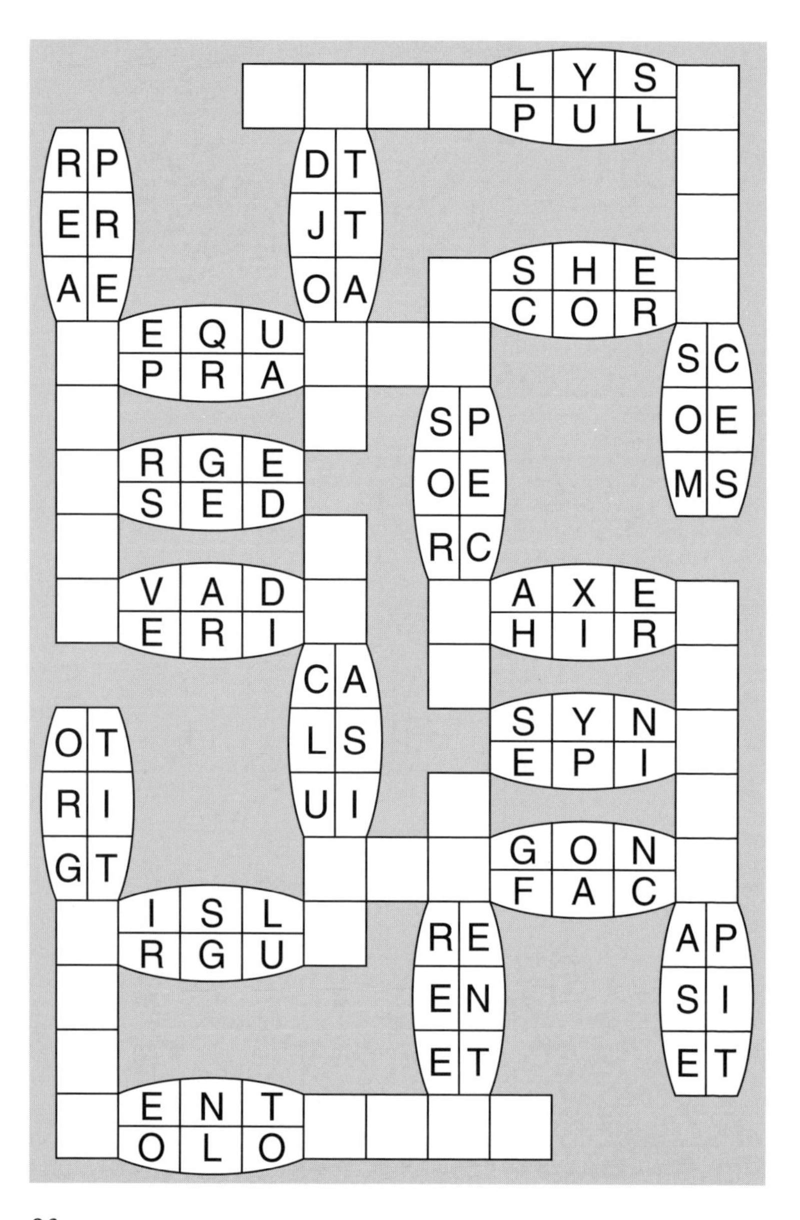

THE FINAL WORD

Directions, page 6 *Answer, page 86*

1

T B E D = _ _ _ _₁

_₁ + A I B I = _ _ _ _ _₂

_₁ _₂ + T I C C = _ _ _ _ _ _₃

_₁ _₂ _₃ + O N I F = _ _ _ _ _ _ _₄

_₁ _₂ _₃ _₄ + L U P U = _ _ _ _ _ _ _ _

The Final Word

"United Metropolitan Improved Hot Muffin and Crumpet Baking and ___ Delivery Company." —Charles Dickens

2

R O U F = _ _ _ _₁

_₁ + A A M D = _ _ _ _ _₂

_₁ _₂ + G E V A = _ _ _ _ _ _₃

_₁ _₂ _₃ + D E T T = _ _ _ _ _ _ _₄

_₁ _₂ _₃ _₄ + E G R N = _ _ _ _ _ _ _ _

The Final Word

"What was good for God's birds was bad for God's ___."
—Thomas Hardy

SPLIT DECISIONS

Directions, page 7 *Answer, page 81*

MIXAGRAMS

Directions, page 7

Answer, page 93

1 Clue: The best way to see a potbelly

↓ ↓

E V A S T E E N R = _ _ _ _ _ + _ _ _ _

S R I S I N E N G = _ _ _ _ _ + _ _ _ _

M E A D A M P O T = _ _ _ _ _ + _ _ _ _

F E A M W U R E D = _ _ _ _ _ + _ _ _ _

2 Clue: Beat generation

↓ ↓

Q U S A L I D D S = _ _ _ _ _ + _ _ _ _

O G U A M R E N D = _ _ _ _ _ + _ _ _ _

L E V A L I U S E = _ _ _ _ _ + _ _ _ _

B A L O O M P Y S = _ _ _ _ _ + _ _ _ _

TWO BY TWO

Directions, page 7

Answer, page 84

SPLIT DECISIONS

Directions, page 7 *Answer, page 89*

TRIAD SPLIT DECISIONS

Directions, page 7 *Answer, page 77*

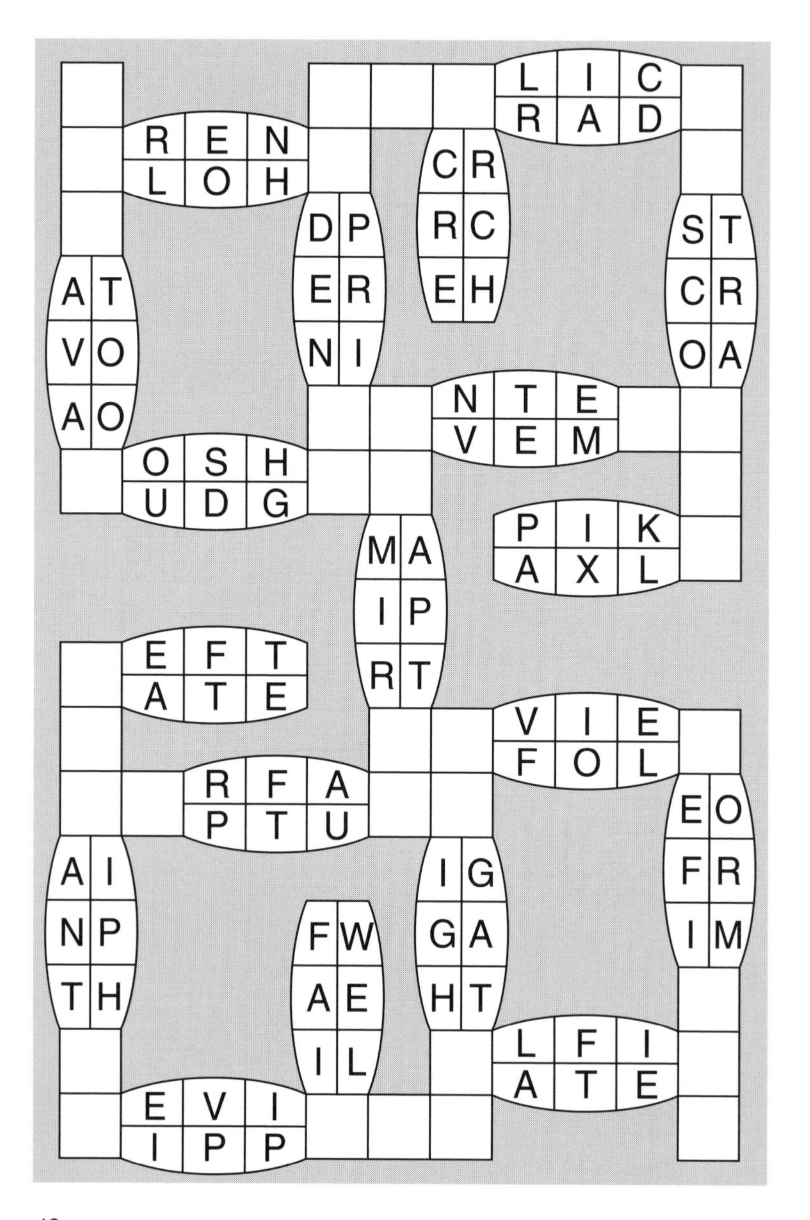

LATTICEWORK

Directions, page 6

Answer, page 87

SPLIT DECISIONS

Directions, page 7 *Answer, page 73*

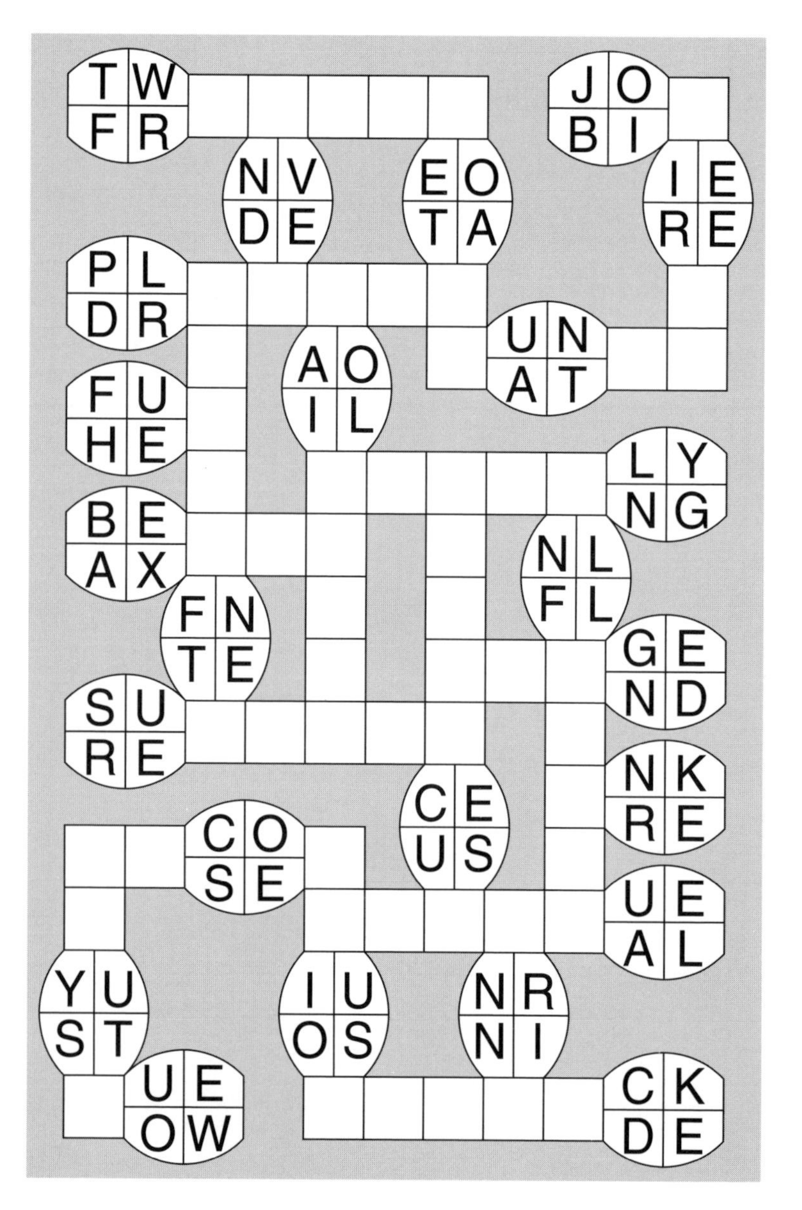

FILL-IN STATION

Directions, page 6 *Answer, page 80*

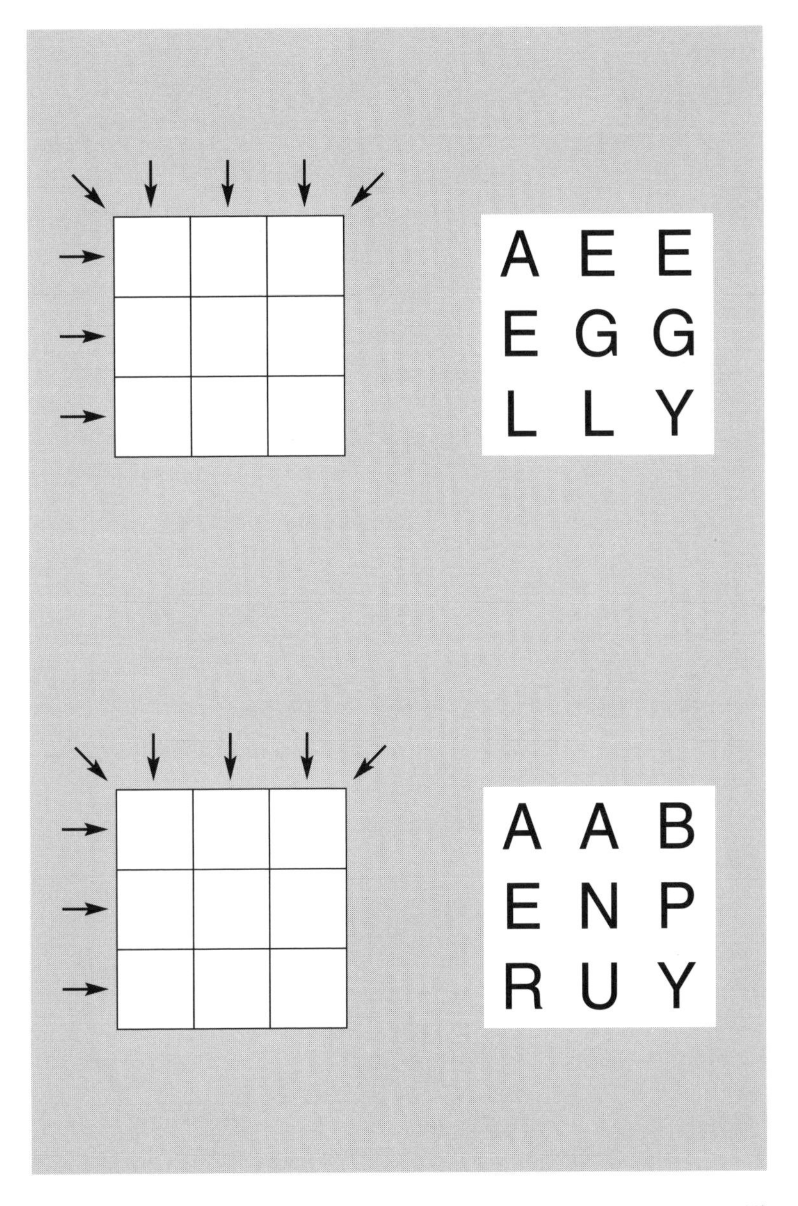

TWO BY TWO

Directions, page 7

Answer, page 82

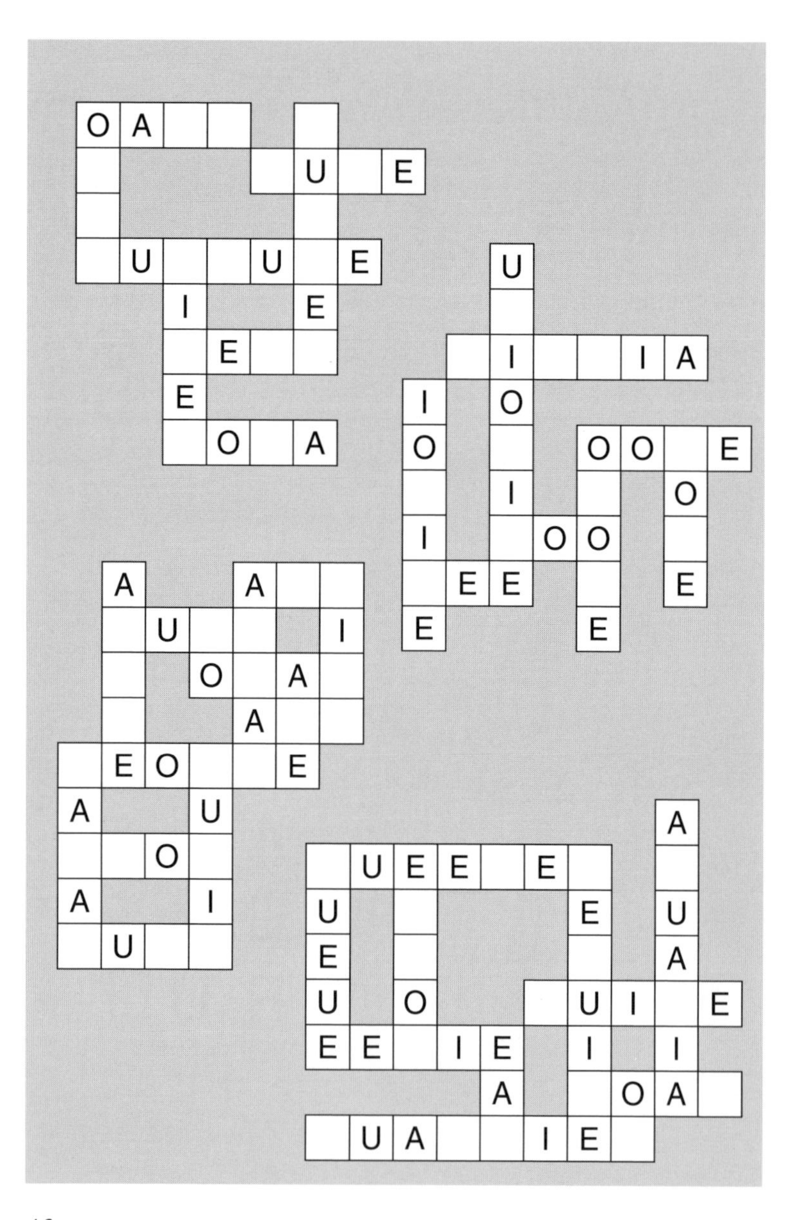

SPLIT DECISIONS

Directions, page 7 *Answer, page 77*

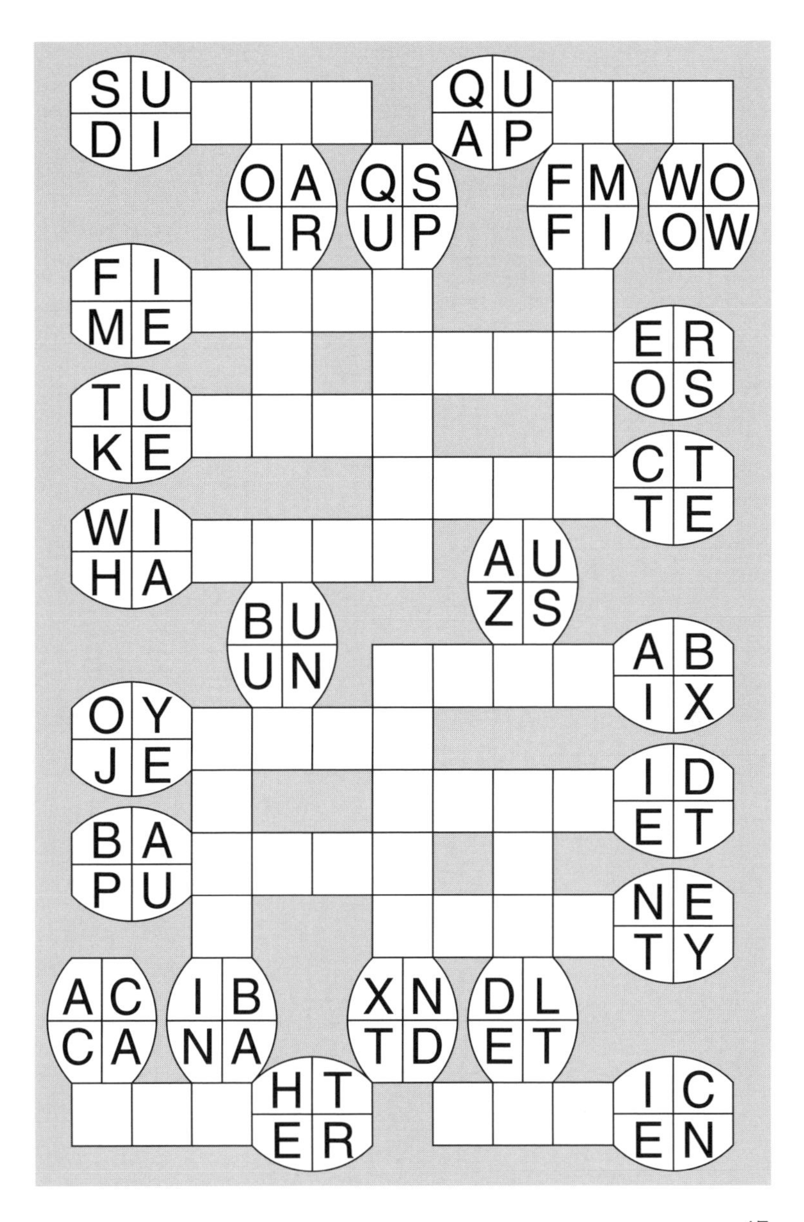

TRIAD SPLIT DECISIONS

Directions, page 7 *Answer, page 91*

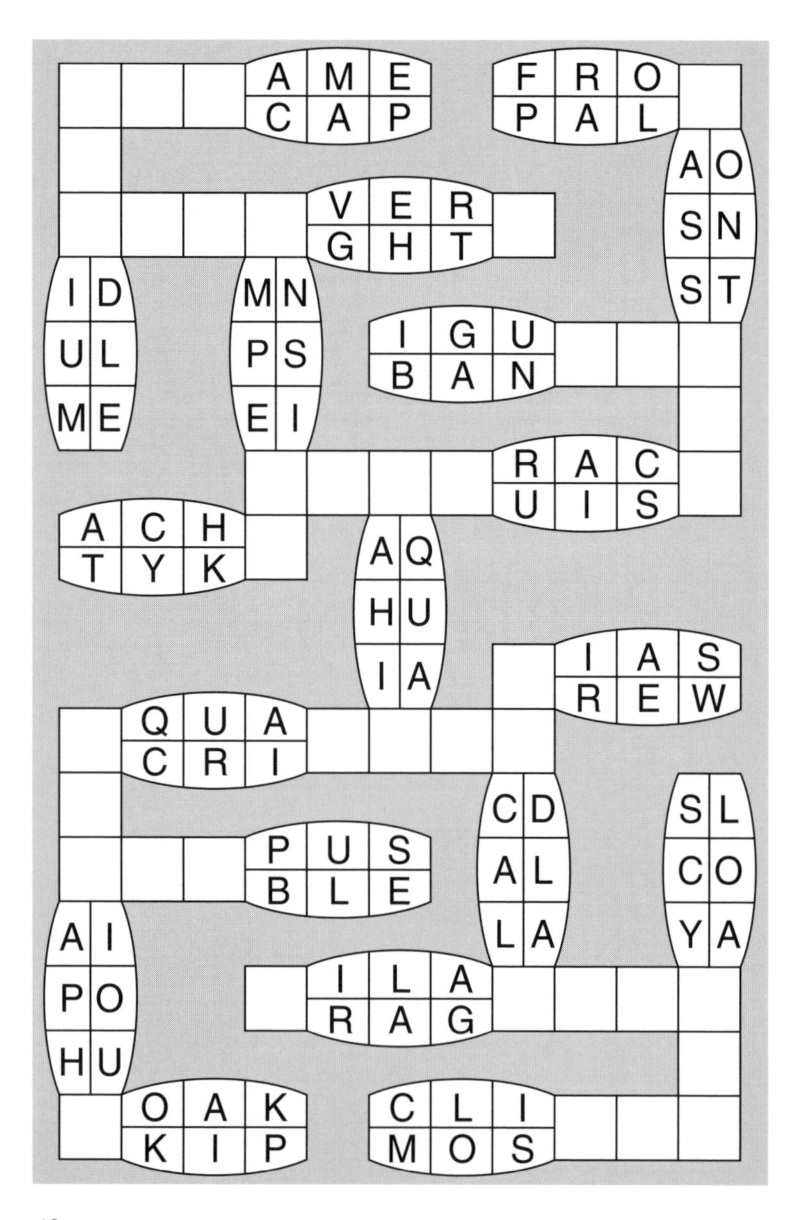

CLUELESS CROSSWORDS

Directions, page 6 *Answer, page 76*

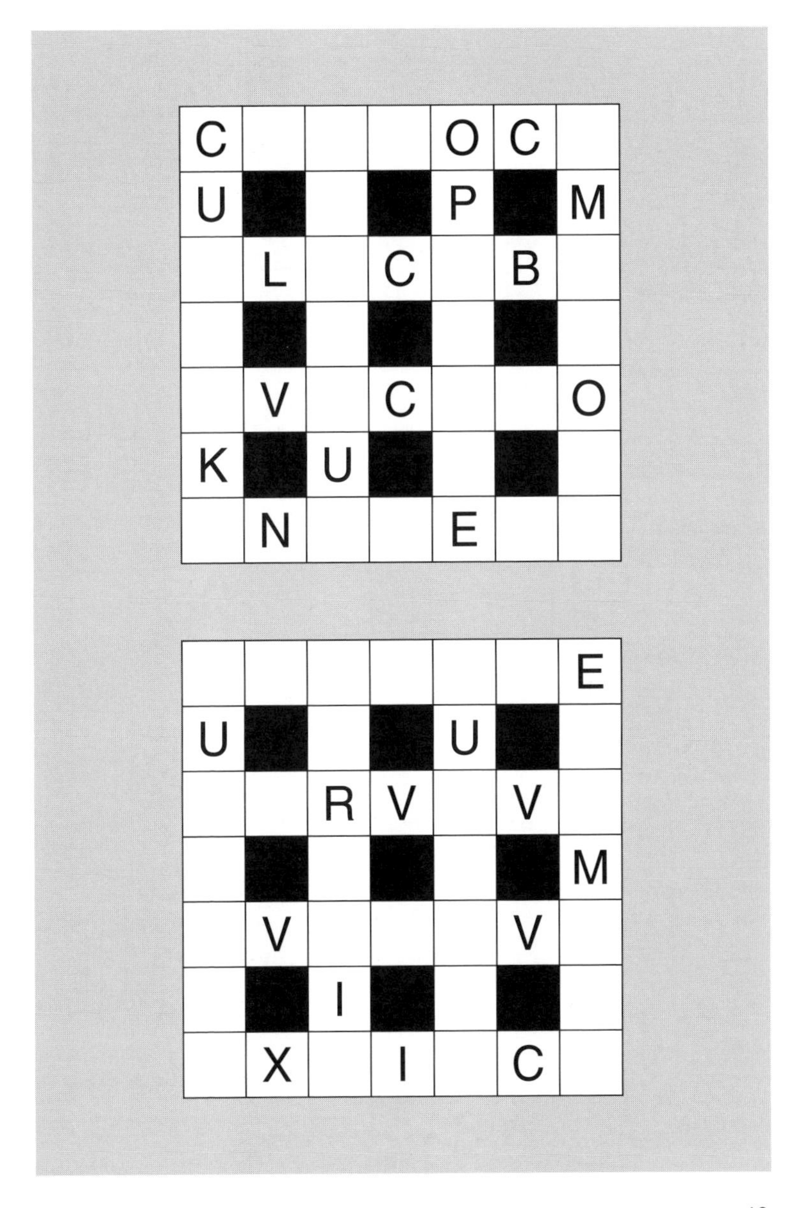

SPLIT DECISIONS

Directions, page 7 *Answer, page 79*

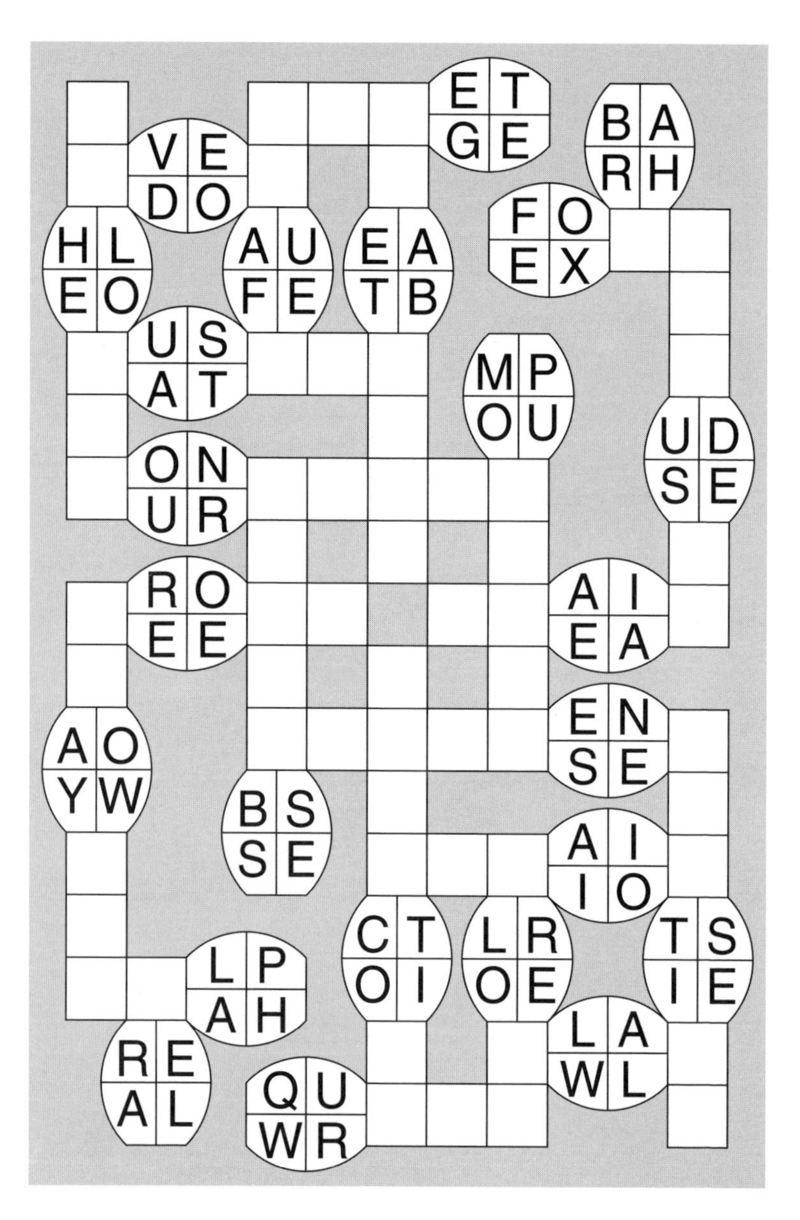

MIXAGRAMS

Directions, page 7 *Answer, page 92*

1 Clue: Invention for walking through walls

↓ ↓

UWONDRIND = _ _ _ _ _ + _ _ _ _

DAIVODOWE = _ _ _ _ _ + _ _ _ _

YABOODEWL = _ _ _ _ _ + _ _ _ _

SCAIRCAKE = _ _ _ _ _ + _ _ _ _

2 Clue: They're better on chests than toes

↓ ↓

DENBASALT = _ _ _ _ _ + _ _ _ _

SAPAPGALA = _ _ _ _ _ + _ _ _ _

BEMERLONG = _ _ _ _ _ + _ _ _ _

HEXIPERST = _ _ _ _ _ + _ _ _ _

TWO BY TWO

Directions, page 7

Answer, page 86

SPLIT DECISIONS

Directions, page 7 *Answer, page 81*

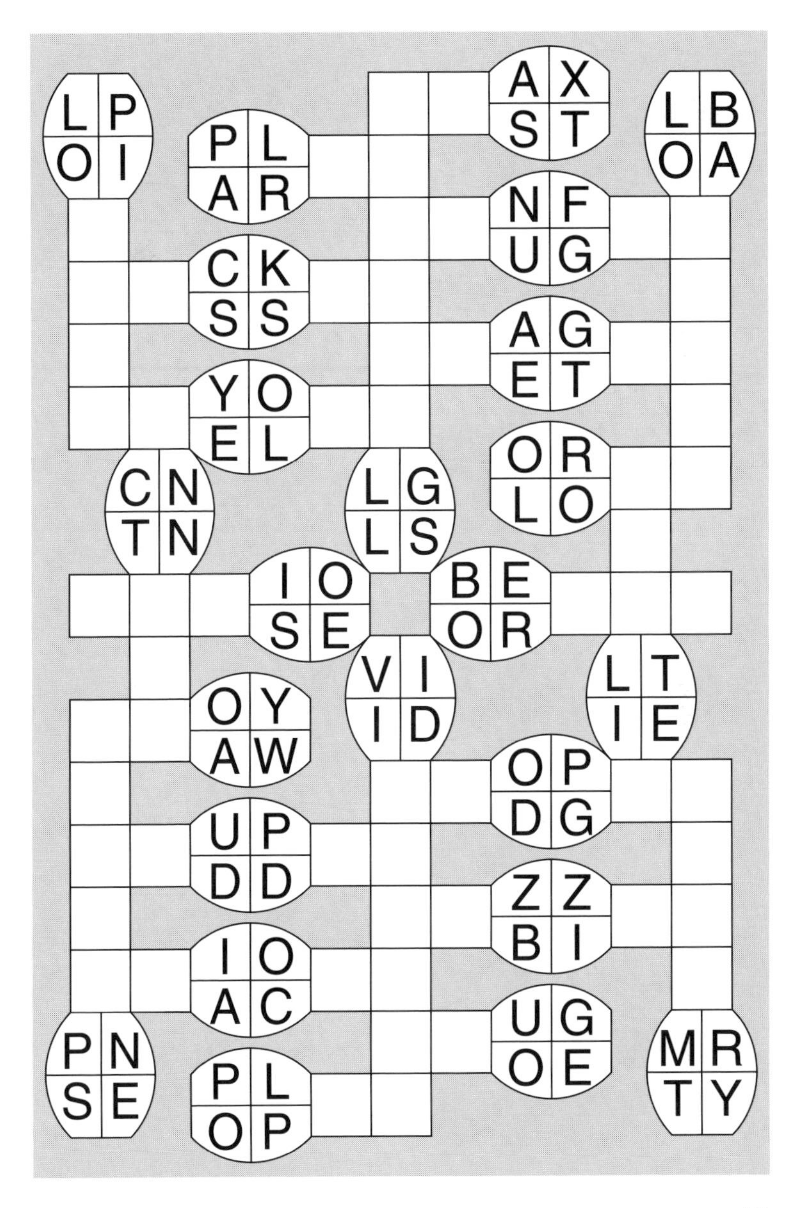

DOUBLE EXPOSURE

Directions, page 6 *Answer, page 84*

1

_ _ _ | _ _ _ _ _ _ _ | _ _ _ _

N	C		R	V					S		J		O
		Q			C	C	C		Y	K			
			K	O		T	H	G		I		D	A
W	R				U					I	X	N	Y
		N		E	A			A	D				
T	H	E	H			G	G	E			S	K	

_ _ _ _ _ _ _ _ _ | _ _ _ _ _

2

_ _ _ _ _ _ _ _ | _ _ _ _ _ _

		V	Z	B	H		L		H	D		Z	
U								P		U	M		N
	S		N	S		M	Y	W				R	J
Z		T				B			B				
	E	R			O	D		R	R		G		Y
R	W		H	P	M		G			X	N	S	

_ _ _ _ _ _ | _ _ _ | _ _ _ _ _

SPLIT DECISIONS

Directions, page 7 *Answer, page 83*

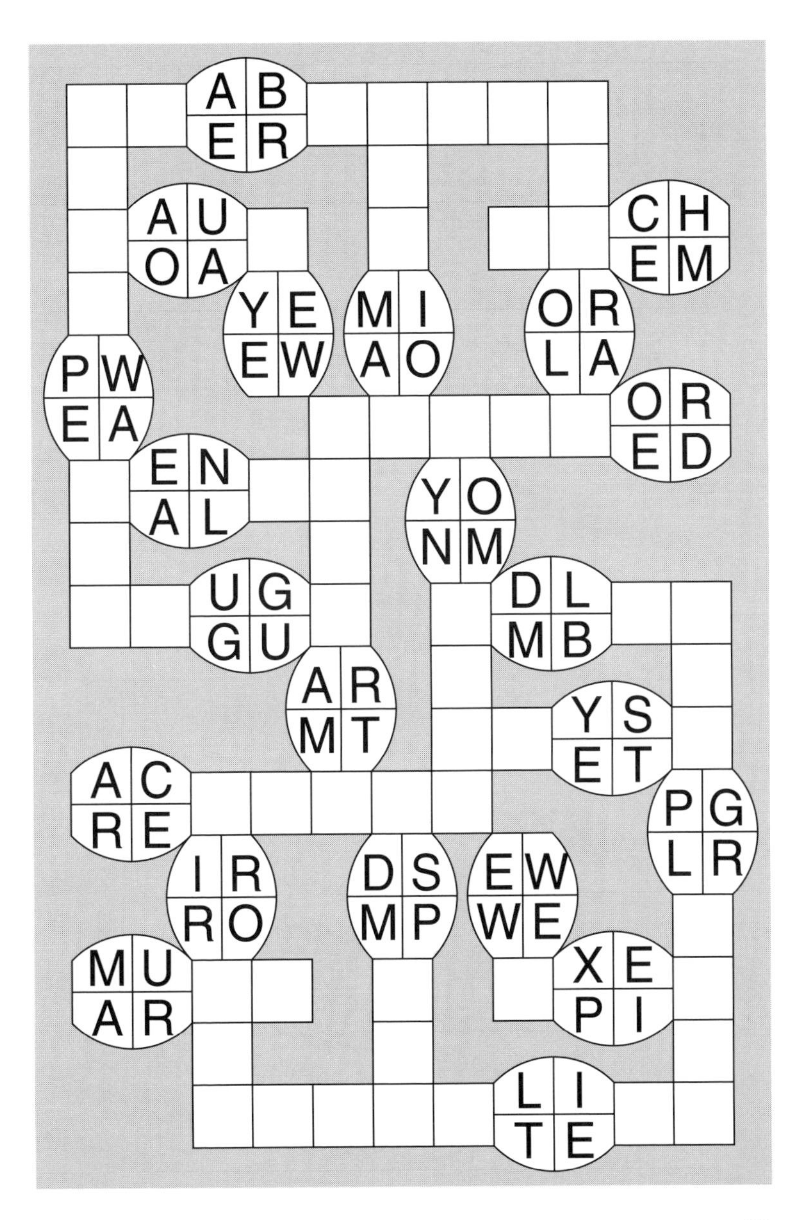

TRIAD SPLIT DECISIONS

Directions, page 7

Answer, page 73

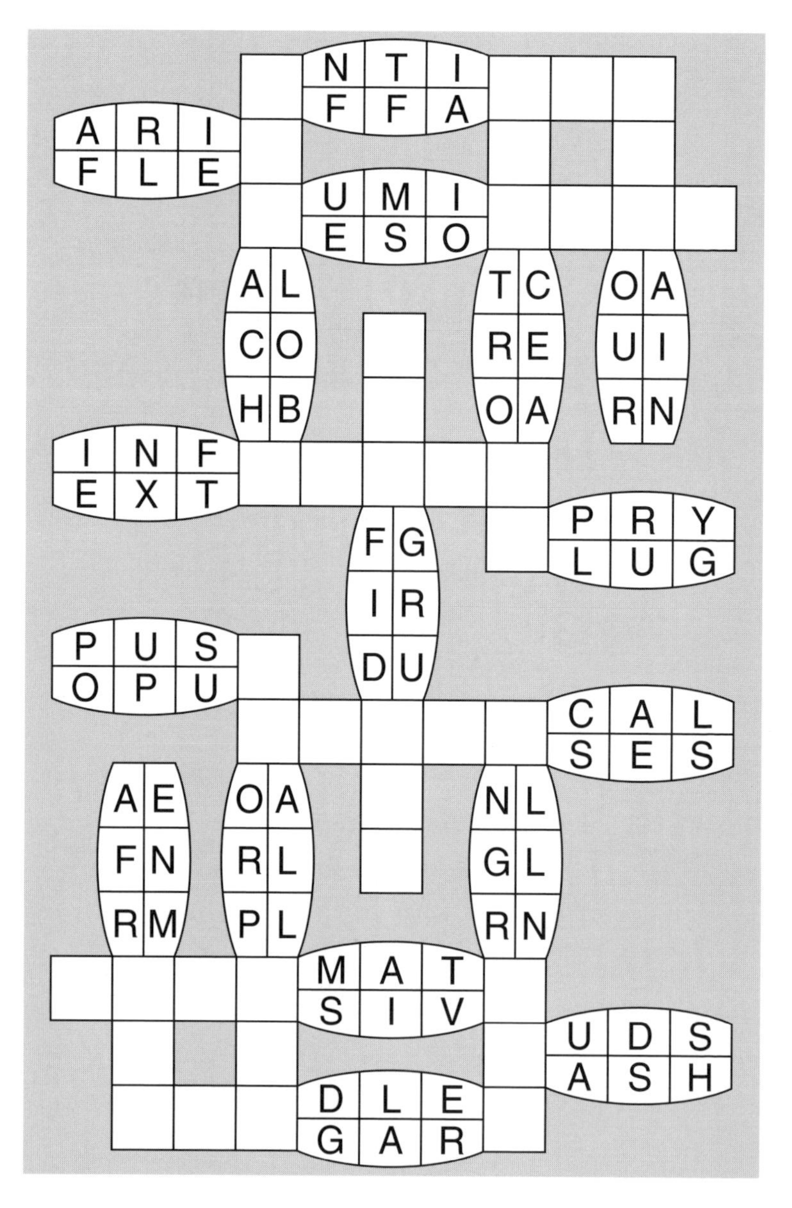

THE FINAL WORD

Directions, page 6 *Answer, page 87*

1

L I R G = _ _ _ _ (1)

_ (1) + N I N E = _ _ _ _ _ (2)

_ _ (1 2) + F E I A = _ _ _ _ _ _ (3)

_ _ _ (1 2 3) + G I L S = _ _ _ _ _ _ _ (4)

_ _ _ _ (1 2 3 4) + I O R I = _ _ _ _ _ _ _ _

The Final Word

"My country is the world, and my ___ is to do good."
—Thomas Paine

2

A N O R = _ _ _ _ (1)

_ (1) + E O S O = _ _ _ _ _ (2)

_ _ (1 2) + L E R K = _ _ _ _ _ _ (3)

_ _ _ (1 2 3) + B U D D = _ _ _ _ _ _ _ (4)

_ _ _ _ (1 2 3 4) + I O U S = _ _ _ _ _ _ _ _

The Final Word

"Fishing is a ___ entirely surrounded by liars in old clothes."
—Don Marquis

SPLIT DECISIONS

Directions, page 7

Answer, page 85

TWO BY TWO

Directions, page 7 *Answer, page 93*

LATTICEWORK

Directions, page 6

Answer, page 88

SPLIT DECISIONS

Directions, page 7 *Answer, page 81*

TRIAD SPLIT DECISIONS

Directions, page 7

Answer, page 83

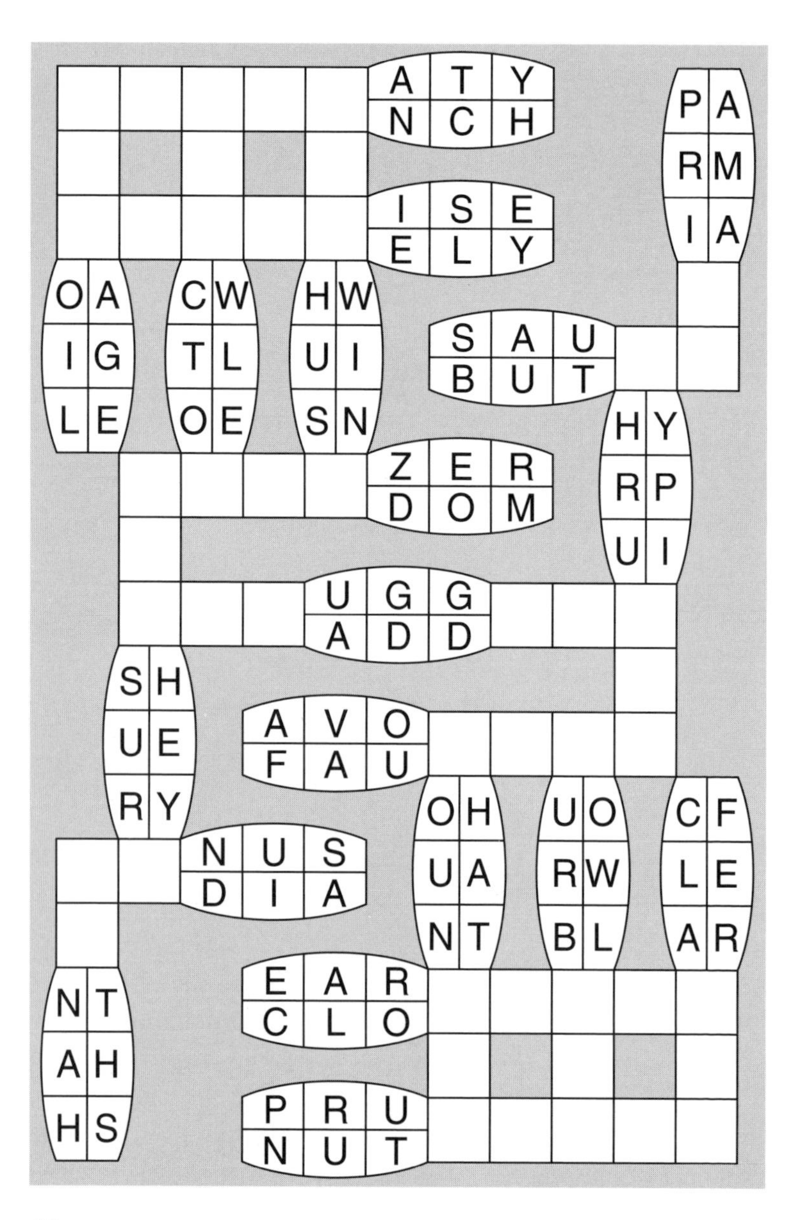

DOUBLE EXPOSURE

Directions, page 6

Answer, page 88

1

_ _ _ _ | _ _ | _ _ _ _ _ | _ _ _

Z	S	E		Q			F		P	K			
			Y		H	G		V			W		Y
		T	E		R	H			C	I		V	S
				L		A	H	N	N				E
Y	V			T			T	G			I	A	
R	A	G	D		G					T	S	T	

_ _ _ _ | _ _ | _ _ _ | _ _ _ _ _

2

_ _ _ _ _ _ _ | _ _ | _ _ | _ _ _

Z	K	P		R	R		V				E	T	T
E	N								R				
		E	I	I	V	X		M	N	Z	C		C
R	A		V	G	V		T		A	O		P	
		G	I			S	U	O		R	G		
						M		Y				C	C

_ _ _ | _ _ _ | _ _ _ _ _ _ _ _

SPLIT DECISIONS

Directions, page 7

Answer, page 73

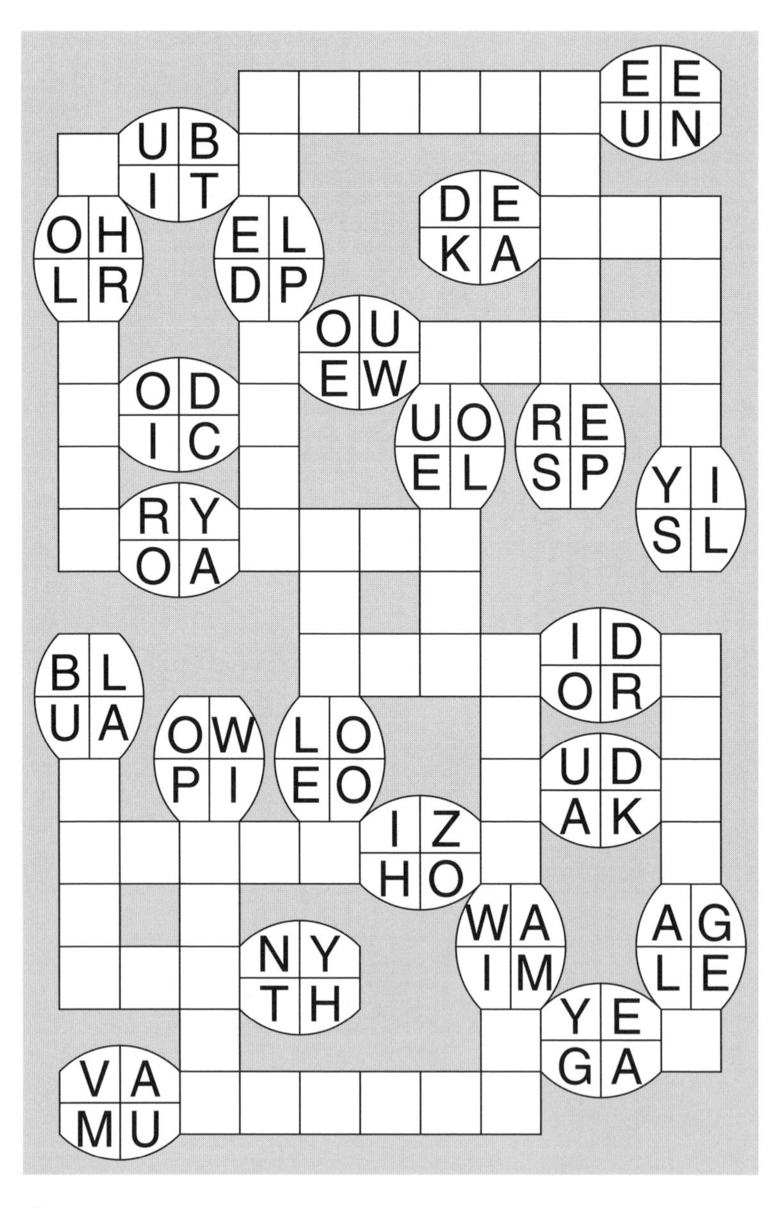

FILL-IN STATION

Directions, page 6 *Answer, page 82*

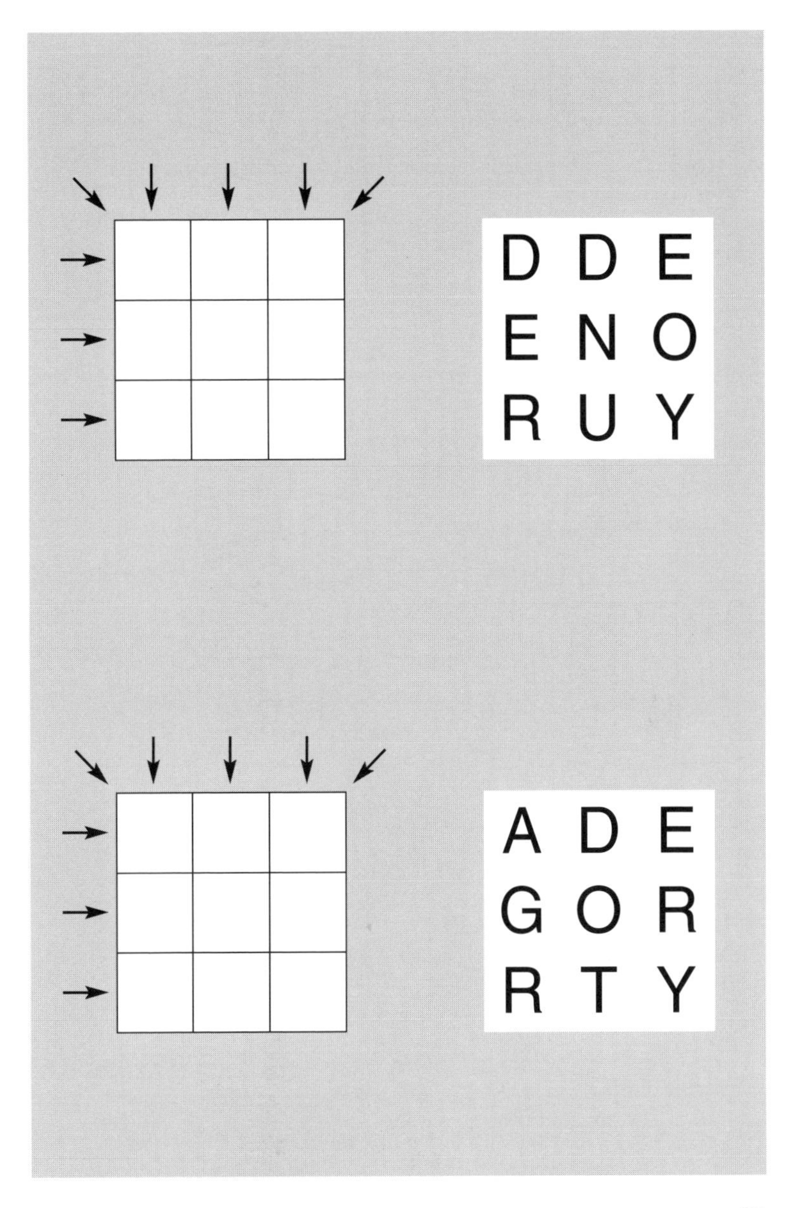

TRIAD SPLIT DECISIONS

Directions, page 7

Answer, page 91

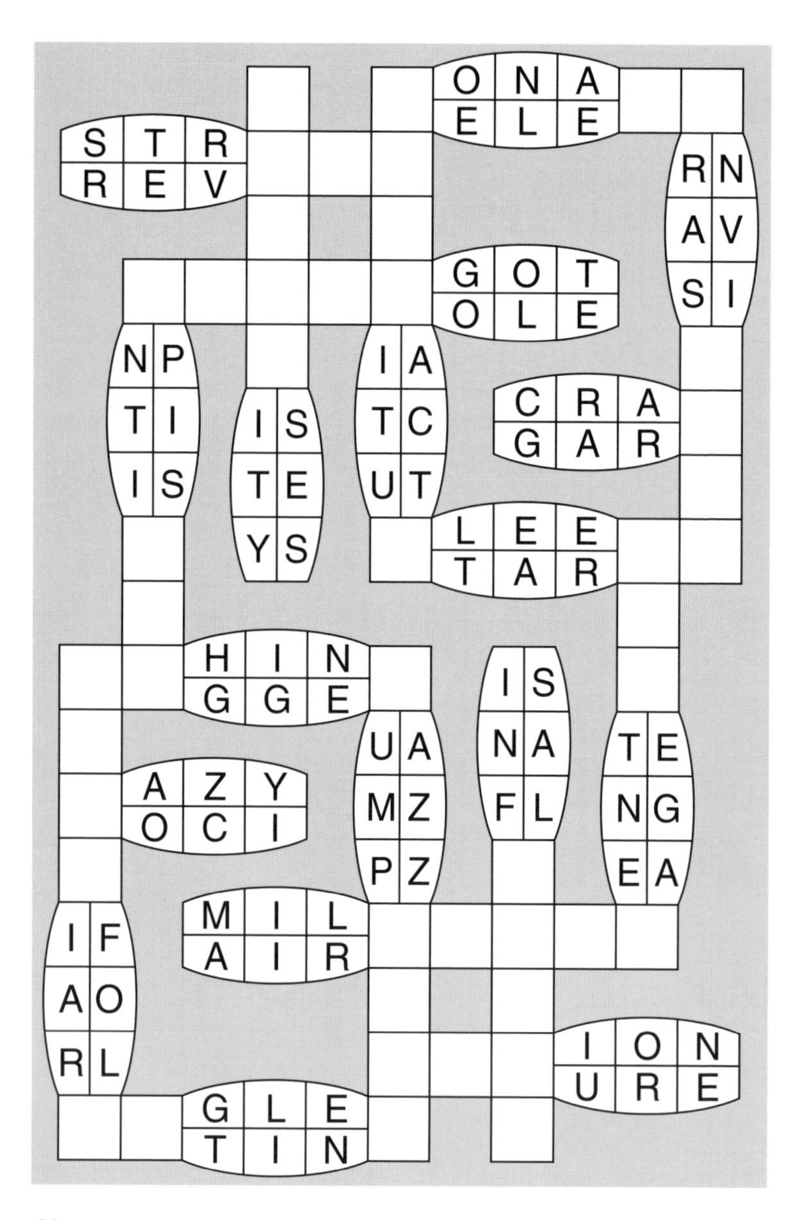

SPLIT DECISIONS

Directions, page 7 *Answer, page 89*

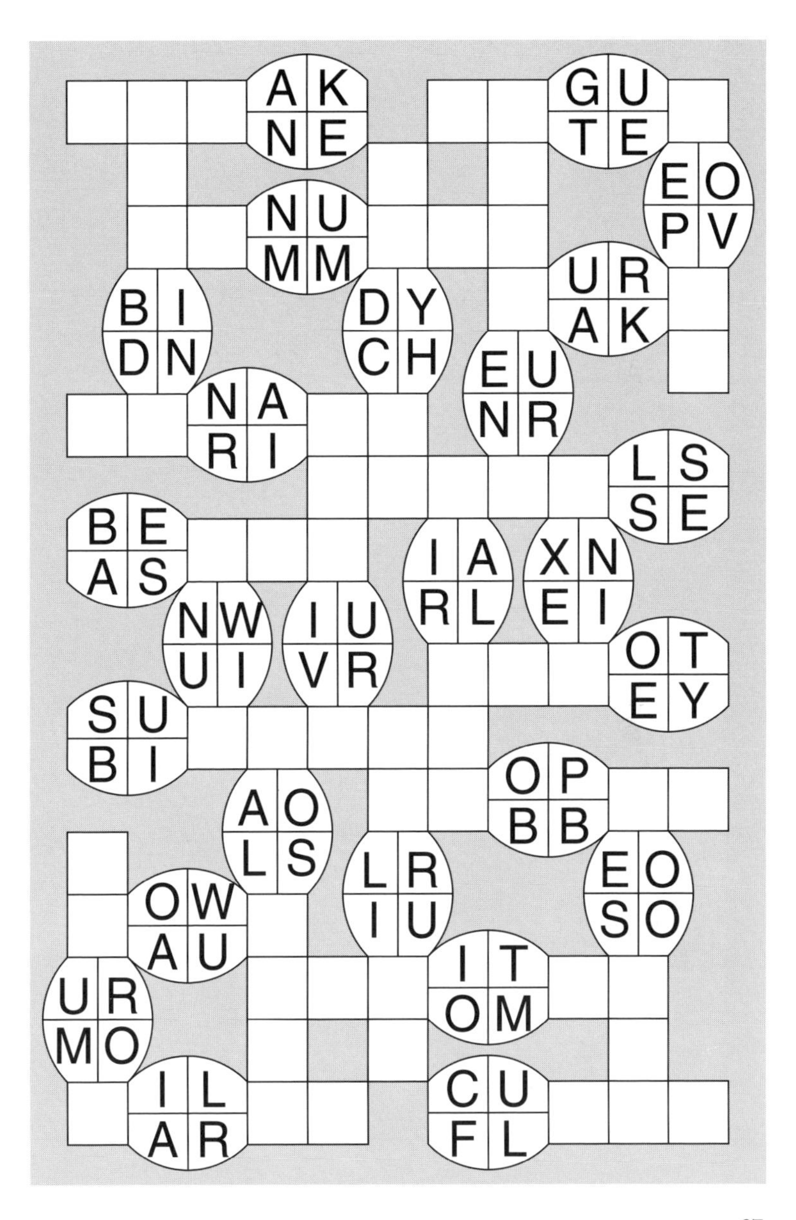

TWO BY TWO

Directions, page 7

Answer, page 76

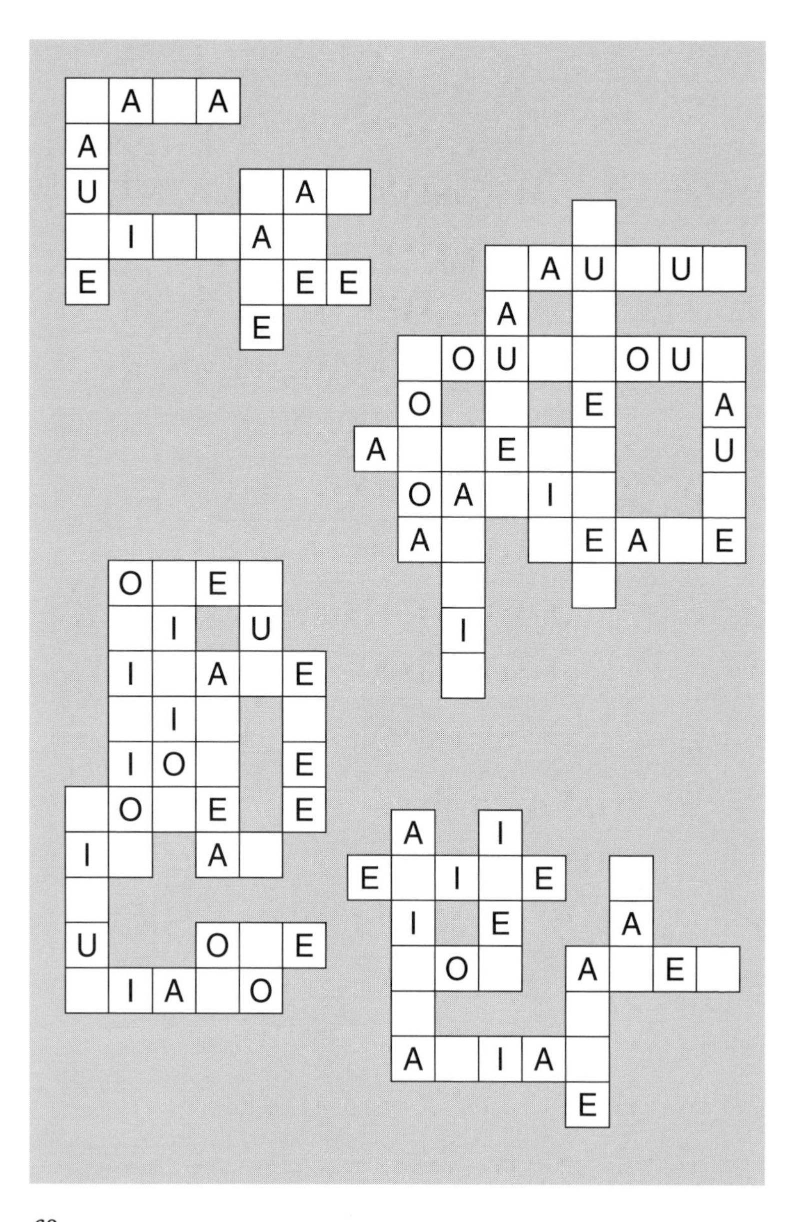

SPLIT DECISIONS

Directions, page 7 *Answer, page 91*

SPLIT DECISIONS

Directions, page 7 *Answer, page 93*

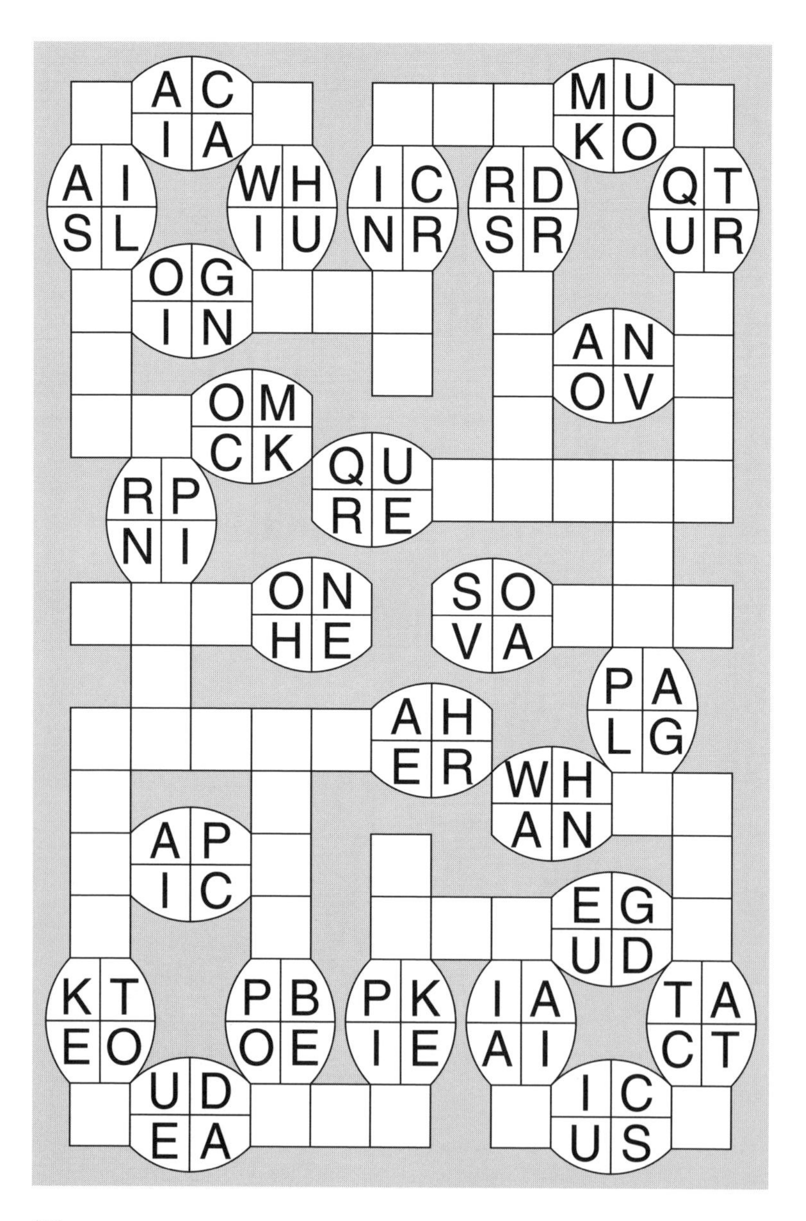

TRIAD SPLIT DECISIONS

Directions, page 7

Answer, page 75

TWO BY TWO

Directions, page 7 *Answer, page 74*

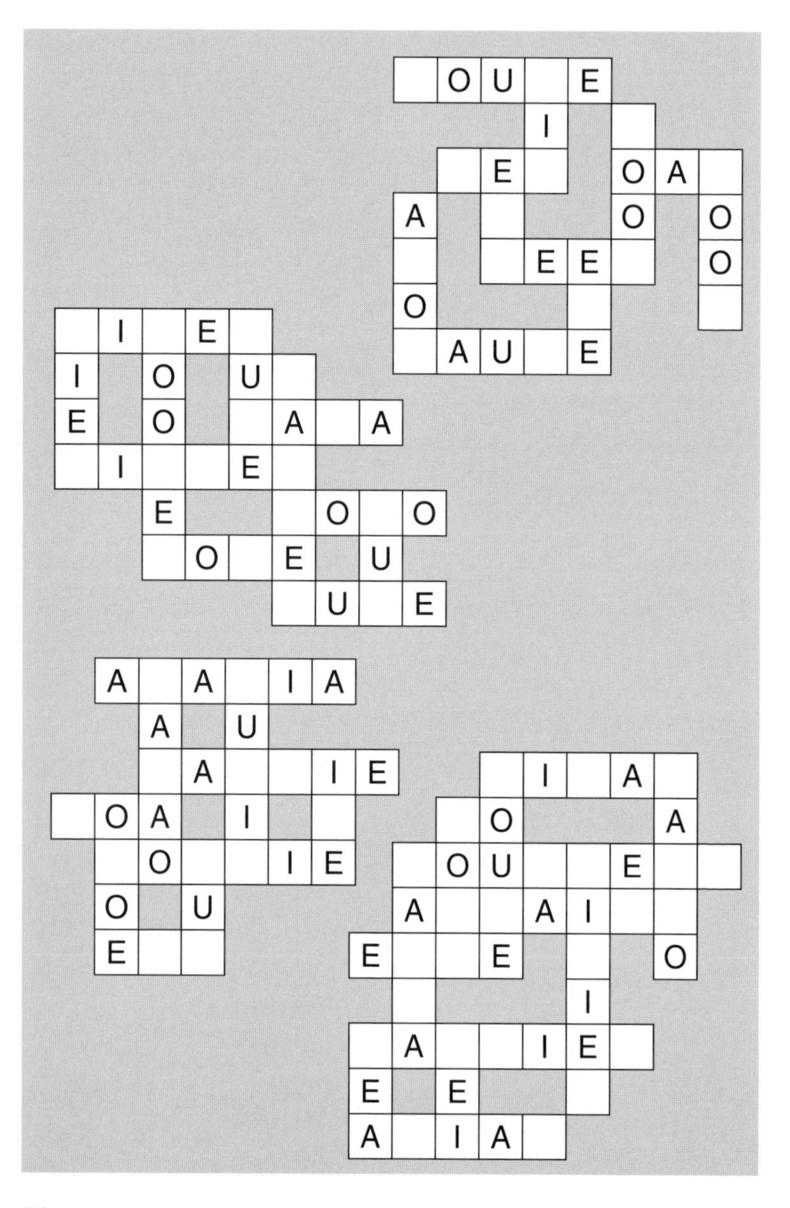

18 SPLIT DECISIONS

44 SPLIT DECISIONS

64 SPLIT DECISIONS

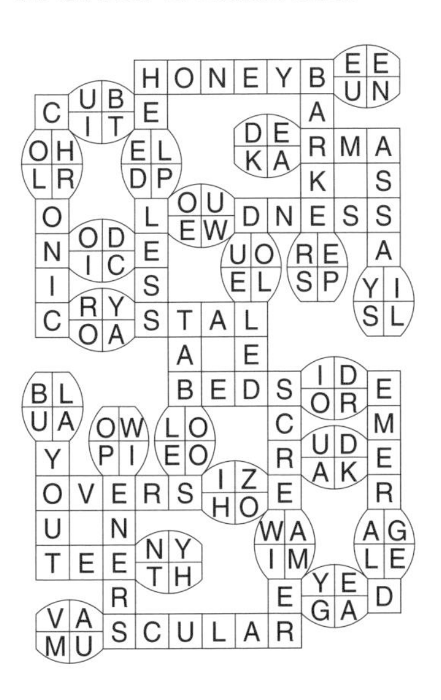

56 TRIAD SPLIT

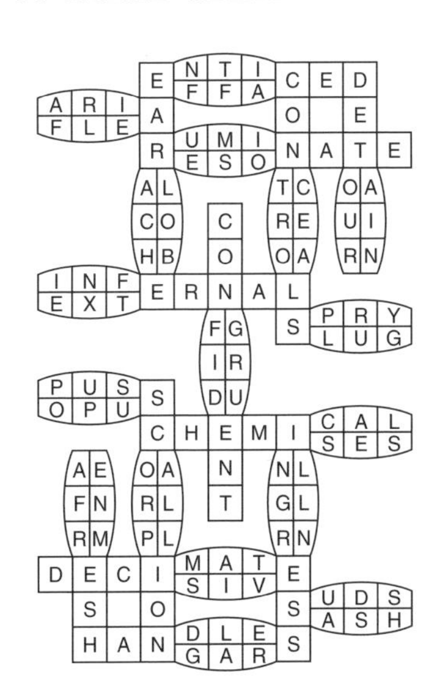

72 TWO BY TWO

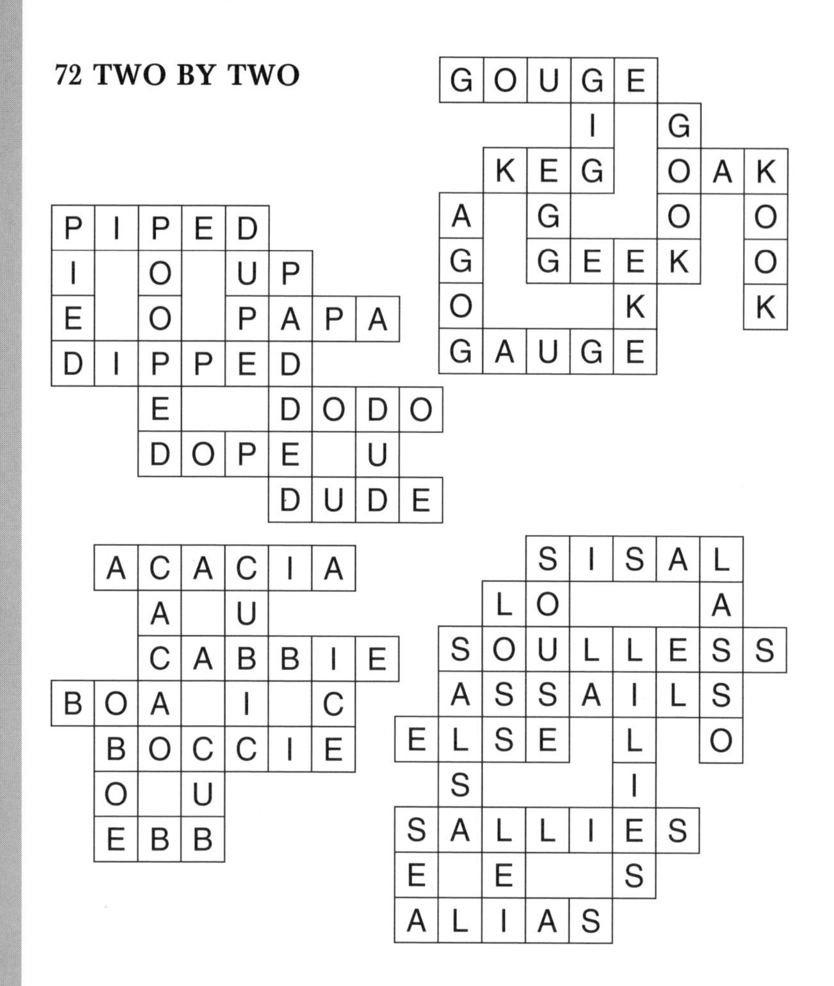

19 DOUBLE EXPOSURE

1 MASHED POTATOES; THE PURPLE HEART
MARKET, WRAITH, SEXIER, WHOOPS, TEDIUM, DWARFS, PEOPLE, NOZZLE, TAXIED, GRAPHS, TWOFER, CLOAKS, WEIRDO, ESPRIT

2 SHARE THE WEALTH; NEW YORK YANKEES
SPHINX, WHENCE, SPAWNS, AIRWAY, VENOMS, UPTURN, SHRIEK, SNEAKY, THWART, EGGNOG, KHAKIS, CLIQUE, JITNEY, SCHISM

15 SPLIT DECISIONS

32 SPLIT DECISIONS

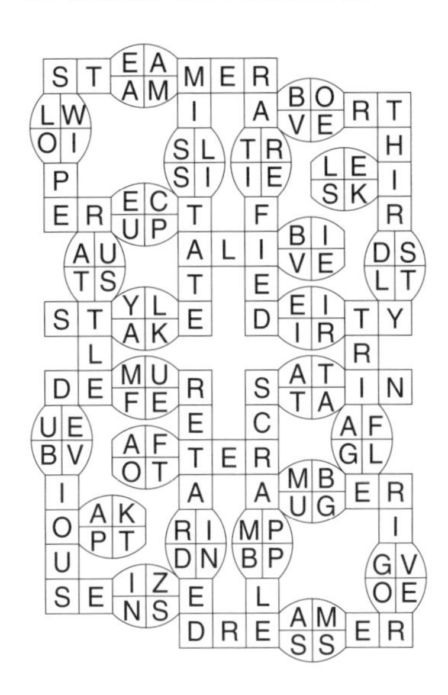

11 TRIAD SPLIT

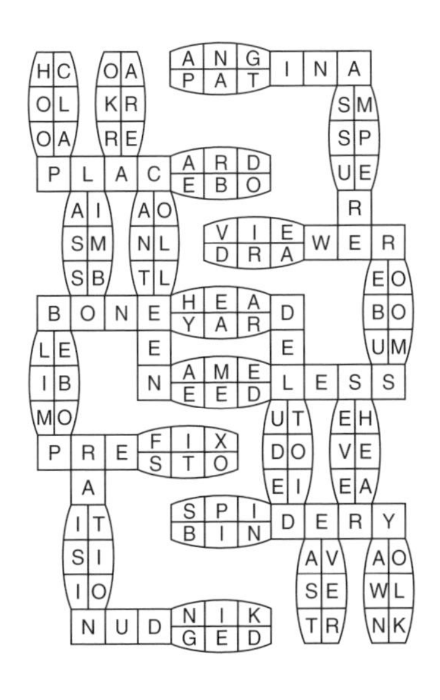

71 TRIAD SPLIT

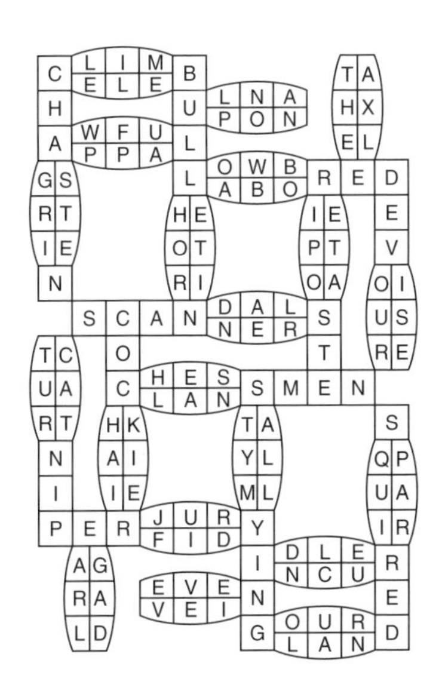

68 TWO BY TWO

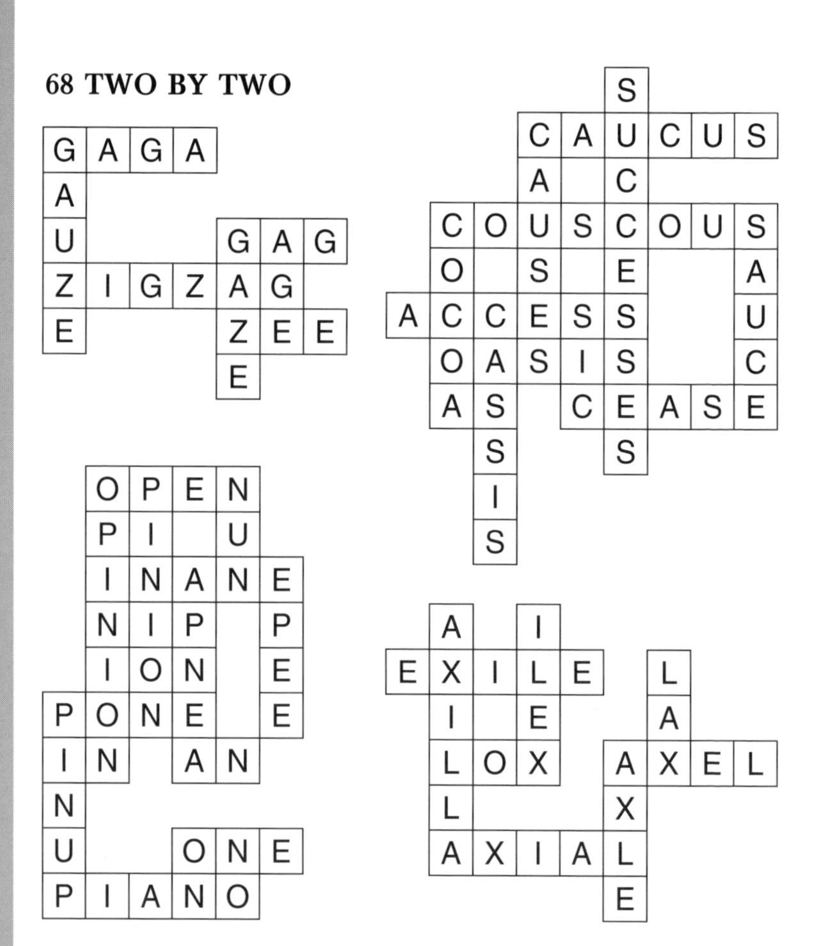

49 CLUELESS CROSSWORDS

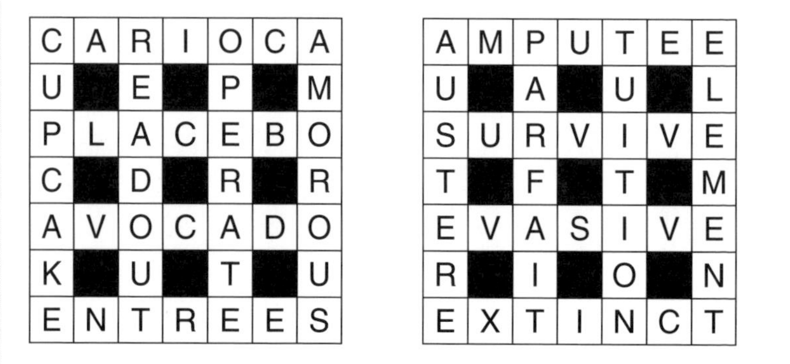

24 SPLIT DECISIONS

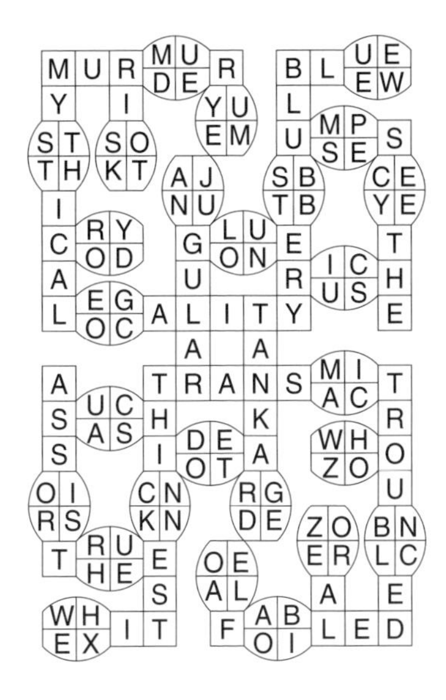

47 SPLIT DECISIONS

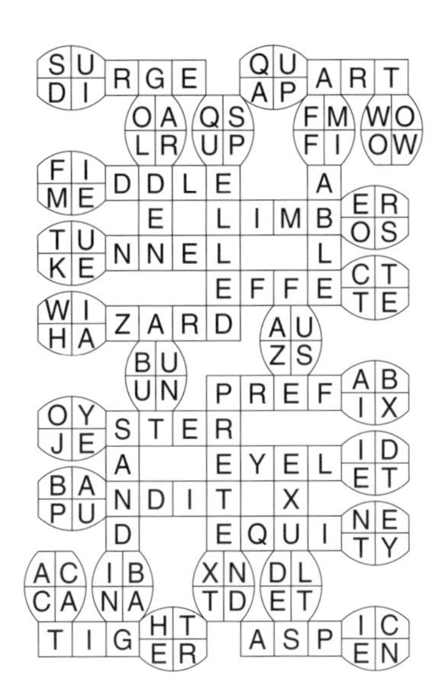

16 TRIAD SPLIT

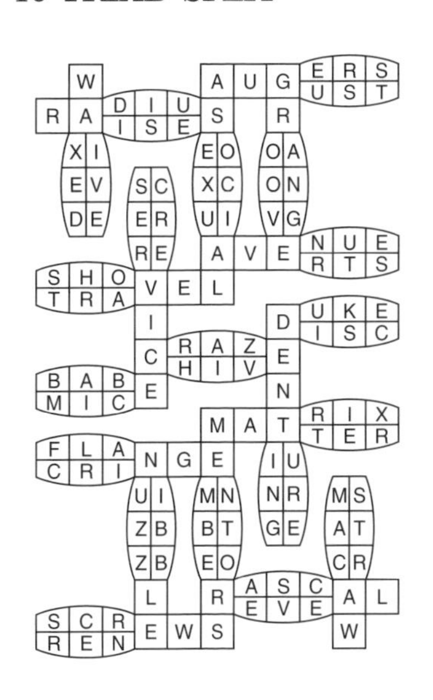

42 TRIAD SPLIT

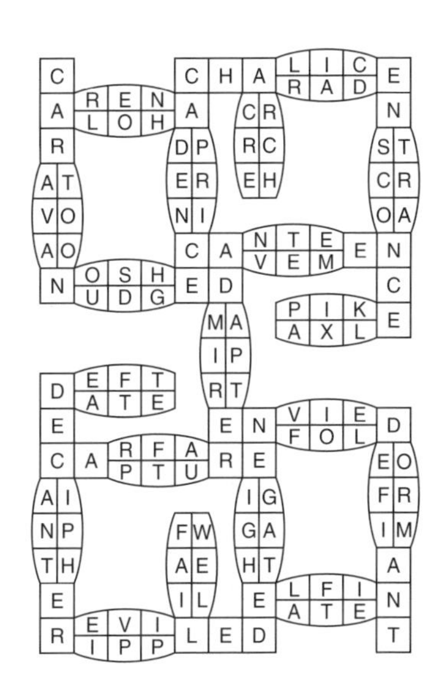

33 TWO BY TWO

N		M	O	N	O	M	A	N	I	A		
O		I		O			N			M		
M	I	N	I	O	N		E			M		
I		I		N			M	E	M	O		
N	A	M	E				O	M	E	N		
E	M	U		A	M	E	N		N	I	N	E
E		M	A	N	E		E			A		

A	S	S	E	S	S
	E			E	
	I			E	
	Z	O	O	S	
	E		O		
			Z		
S	I	Z	E	S	
			S		

O	P	A	Q	U	E	
			U		Q	
		P	I	Q	U	E
			P		I	
		Q	U	I	P	

	A					W
	V	I	E	W		A
	O		W	E		V
	W		E	A	V	E
				V		
W	A	I	V	E		

8 CLUELESS CROSSWORDS

R	E	S	I	D	E	D
E		T		E		E
G	R	O	O	V	E	S
U		P		I		I
L	O	G	J	A	M	S
A		A		T		T
R	E	P	R	E	S	S

S	E	A	L	A	N	T
W		L		R		A
A	I	L	E	R	O	N
R		E		A		K
M	A	G	E	N	T	A
E		E		G		R
D	E	S	C	E	N	D

28 MIXAGRAMS
CAROM + ERGO
VOGUE + DOER
CABIN + ROTS
SINUS + AMID
MEN'S ROOM

GULCH + GLUM
VOICE + DORM
MOCHA + SCUM
SHARD + AKIN
HEAD LOCK

50 SPLIT DECISIONS

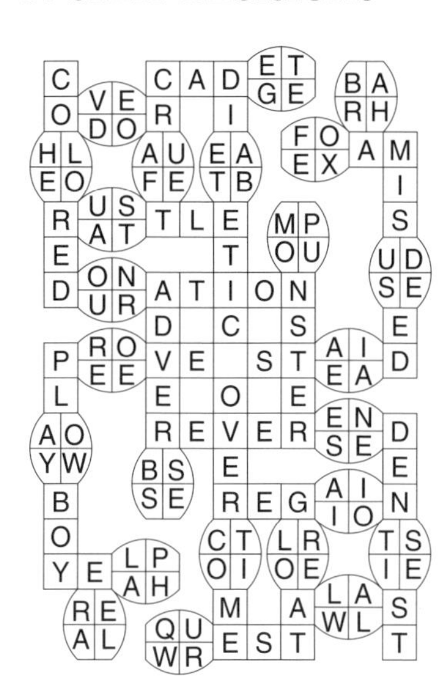

25 TWO BY TWO

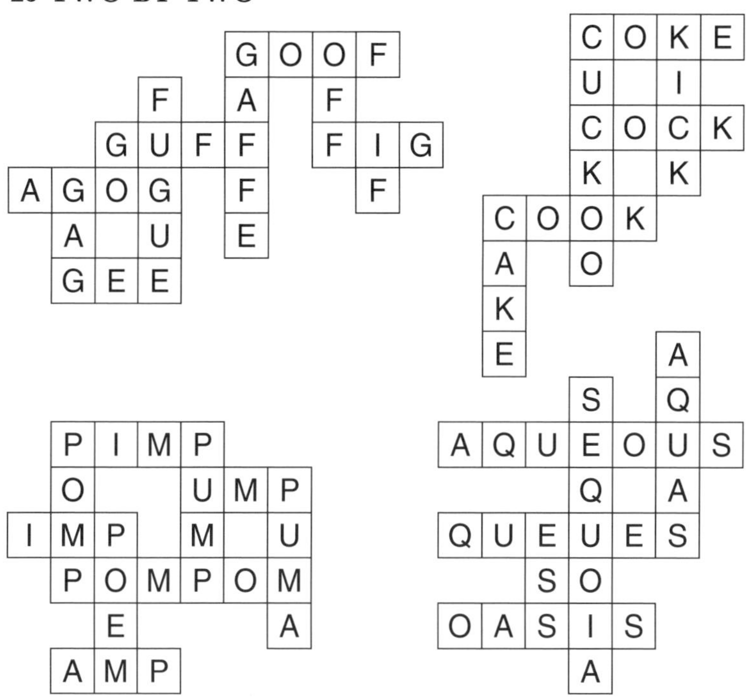

31 LATTICEWORK

			D			M				U		F
			A		C	O	U	S	I	N		A
			U			T				C		T
			G			H				L		H
			H			E		N	I	E	C	E
B	R	O	T	H	E	R		E				R
			E					P				
			R					H				
				S	I	S	T	E	R			
				O				W				
		A	U	N	T							

45 FILL-IN STATION

E	G	G
Y	E	A
E	L	L

P	U	B
E	R	A
A	N	Y

						S					
					G	E	N	E	R	A	L
						R					I
						G					E
	C	O	L	O	N	E	L				U
	O					A					T
	R					N					E
	P	R	I	V	A	T	E				N
	O										A
	R				C	A	P	T	A	I	N
M	A	J	O	R							T
	L										

34 DOUBLE EXPOSURE

1 THE STOCK MARKET; VERY TRULY YOURS
VOTIVE, AWHILE, EXTRAS, SCURVY, TRUANT, JOKERS, CATSUP, MUKLUK, EMPLOY, LAZILY, JARGON, MAKEUP, SWERVE, TRUISM

2 COUNTRY BUMPKIN; KNIVES AND FORKS
JACKAL, BOXING, NUCLEI, CONVOY, ZITHER, ROBUST, SYLVAN, SUBORN, JUDGED, ARMFUL, PSYCHO, SKIERS, PICKUP, CYNICS

29 SPLIT DECISIONS

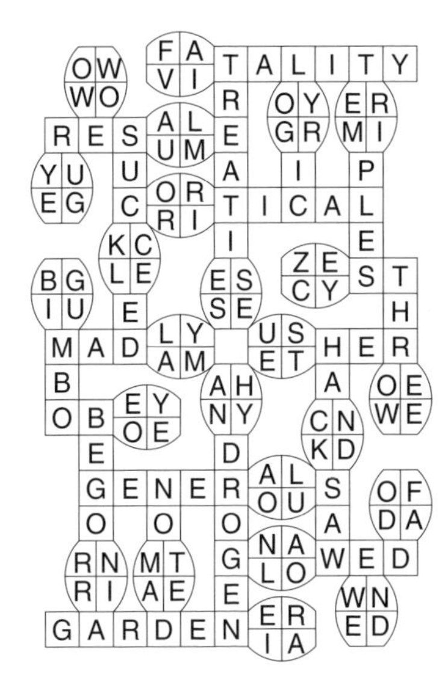

38 SPLIT DECISIONS

53 SPLIT DECISIONS

61 SPLIT DECISIONS

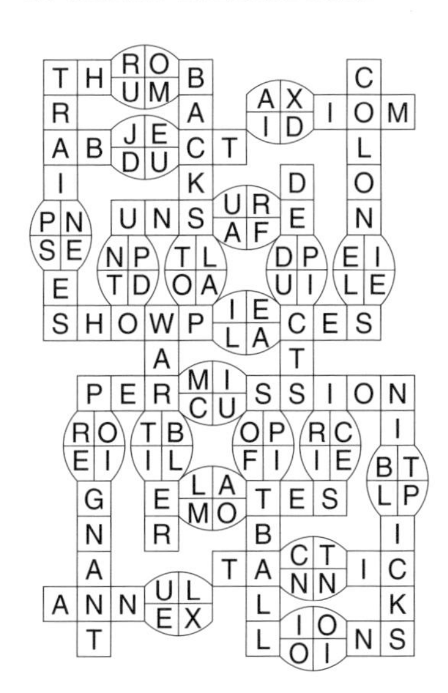

46 TWO BY TWO

O	A	F	S		F		
F				F	U	S	E
F					S		
S	U	F	F	U	S	E	
		I			E		
		F	E	S	S		
		E					
		S	O	F	A		

		U					
		N					
	Z	I	N	N	I	A	
I		O					
O		N		O	O	Z	E
N		I		Z		O	
I		Z	O	O		N	
Z	E	E		N		E	
E				E			

	A			A	L	P
	P	U	L	P		I
	P		O	P	A	L
	L			A	L	L
P	E	O	P	L	E	
A			U			
P	L	O	P			
A			I			
L	U	L	L			

								A	
Q	U	E	E	R	E	R		Q	
U		R				E		U	
E		R				Q		A	
U		O			Q	U	I	R	E
E	E	R	I	E		I		I	
				A		R	O	A	R
Q	U	A	R	R	I	E	R		

65 FILL-IN STATION

R	E	D
Y	O	U
E	N	D

G	E	T
O	A	R
D	R	Y

20 THE FINAL WORD

1 KELP, HIPPO, GOPHER, OPPRESS, PROPHESY

2 UNDO, COUNT, DOCTOR, NEUTRON, DOCTRINE

9 SPLIT DECISIONS

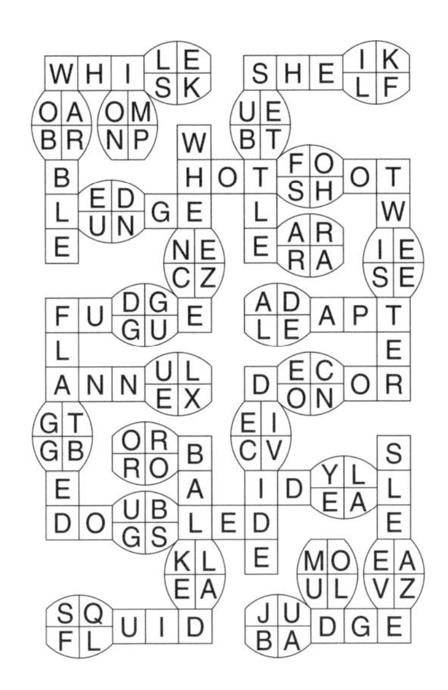

55 SPLIT DECISIONS

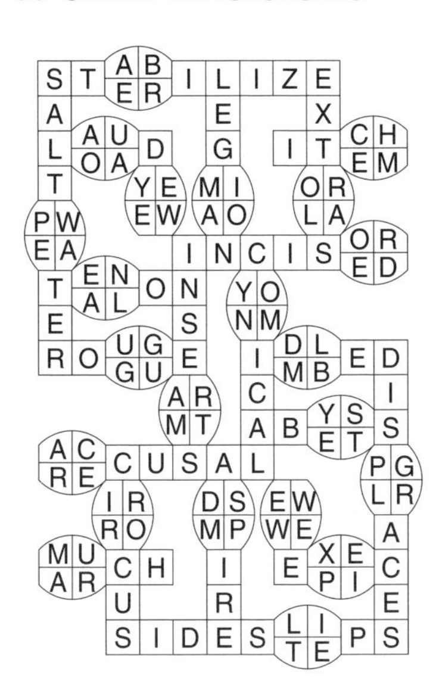

26 TRIAD SPLIT

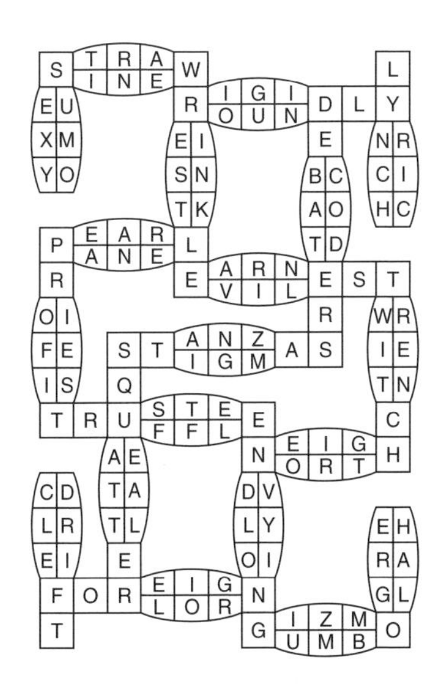

62 TRIAD SPLIT

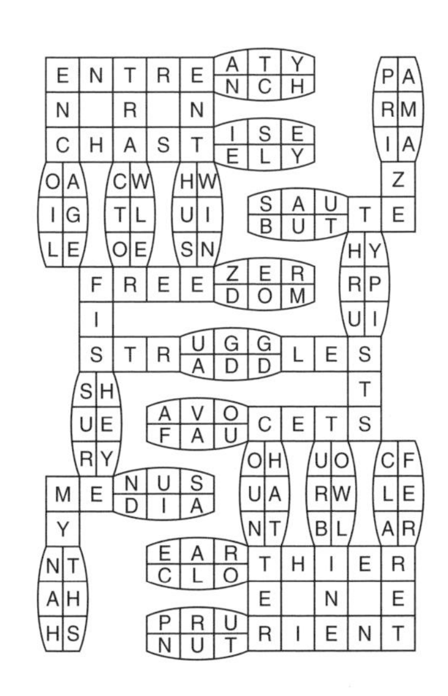

40 TWO BY TWO

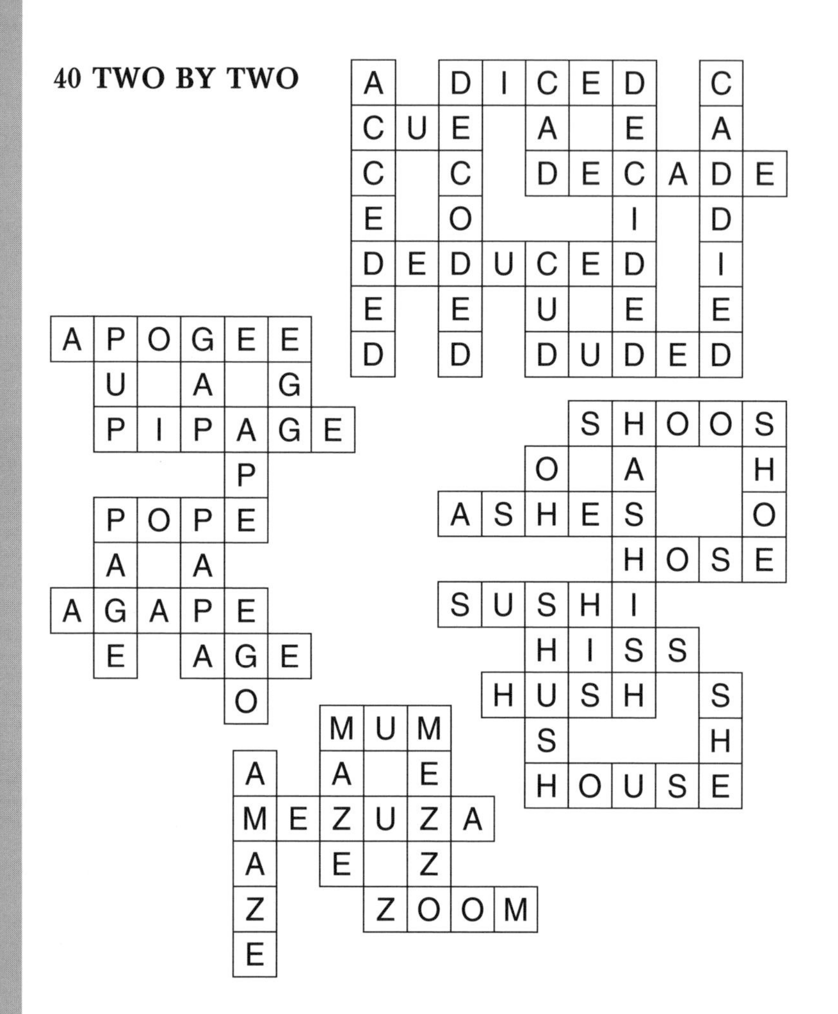

54 DOUBLE EXPOSURE

1 THE KITCHEN SINK; WHISTLING DIXIE
NITWIT, CHURCH, EQUINE, RAKISH, VIOLET, ACTUAL, ACTING, ACHING, REGGAE, SYNODS, SKIING, JINXES, NUDNIK, OKAYED

2 BASEBALL UMPIRE; RHYTHM AND BLUES
BUZZER, CASHEW, VESTRY, ZENITH, BISHOP, HANSOM, LAMBDA, LAYING, UPWARD, HOMBRE, DUPLEX, IMPUGN, ZEROES, ENJOYS

35 SPLIT DECISIONS

58 SPLIT DECISIONS

22 TRIAD SPLIT

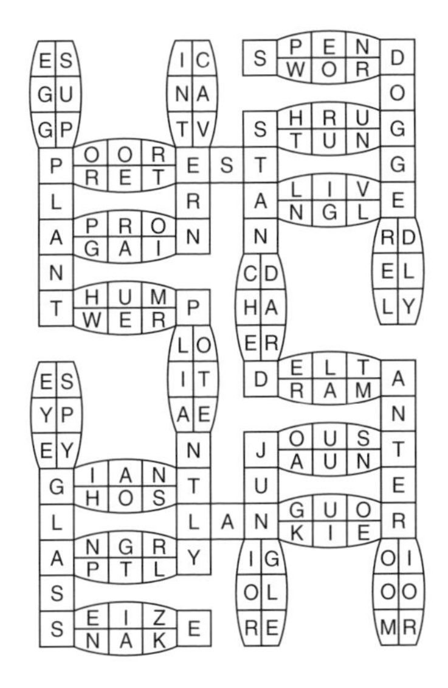

30 TRIAD SPLIT

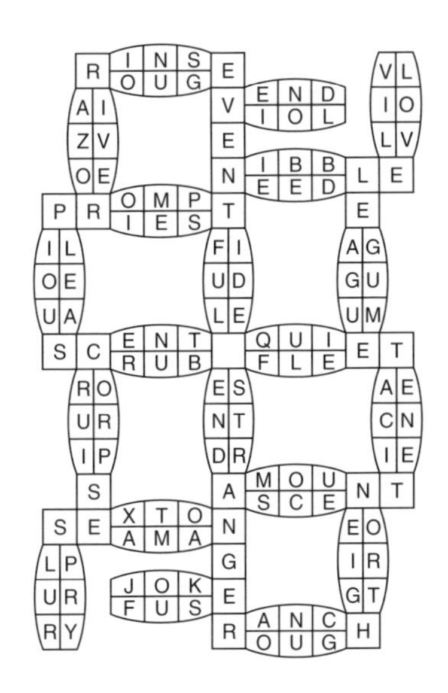

52 TWO BY TWO

14 FRAZE-IT

1 MOOING; KNEE
2 EYEBALL; NURSE
3 IGNORE; SLUSH
MONKEY BUSINESS

1 GROAN; ELBOW
2 VISIT; HATCH
3 MEOW; SINNED
GONE WITH THE WIND

37 THE FINAL WORD

1 DEBT, TIBIA, TACTIC, FACTION, PUNCTUAL
2 FOUR, DRAMA, RAVAGE, TREATED, GARDENER

43 LATTICEWORK

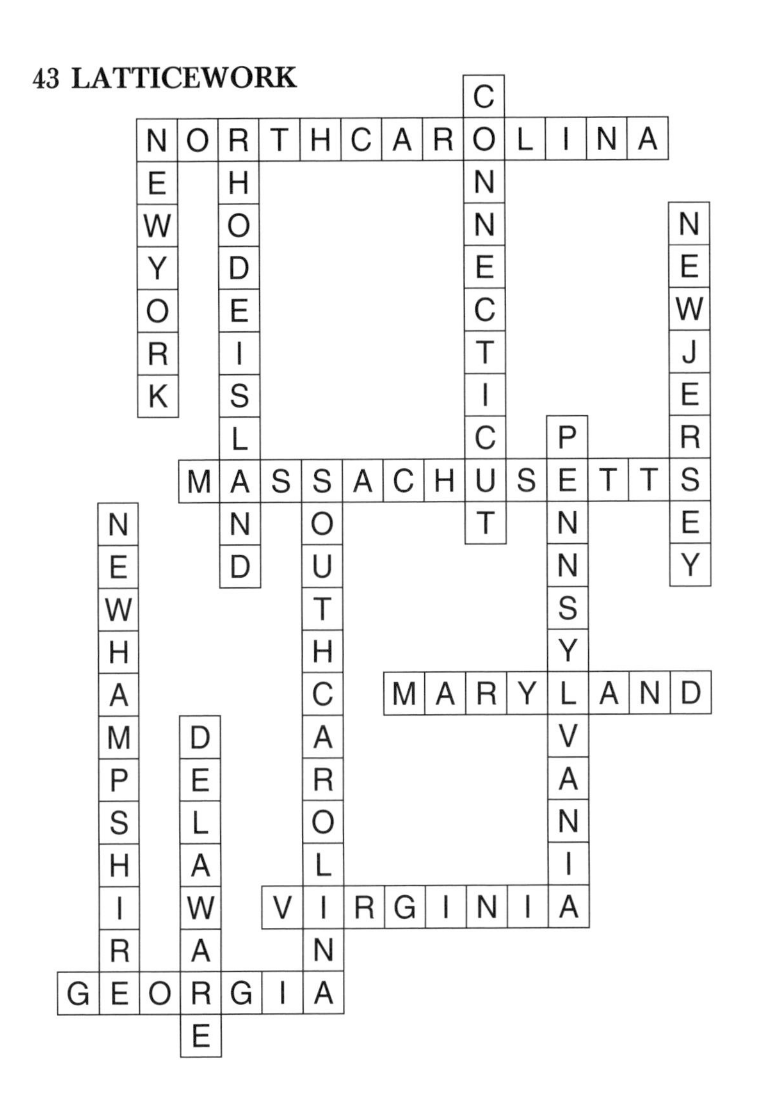

57 THE FINAL WORD

1 GIRL, LINEN, FINALE, SELLING, RELIGION
2 ROAN, NOOSE, KERNEL, BUNDLED, DELUSION

60 LATTICEWORK

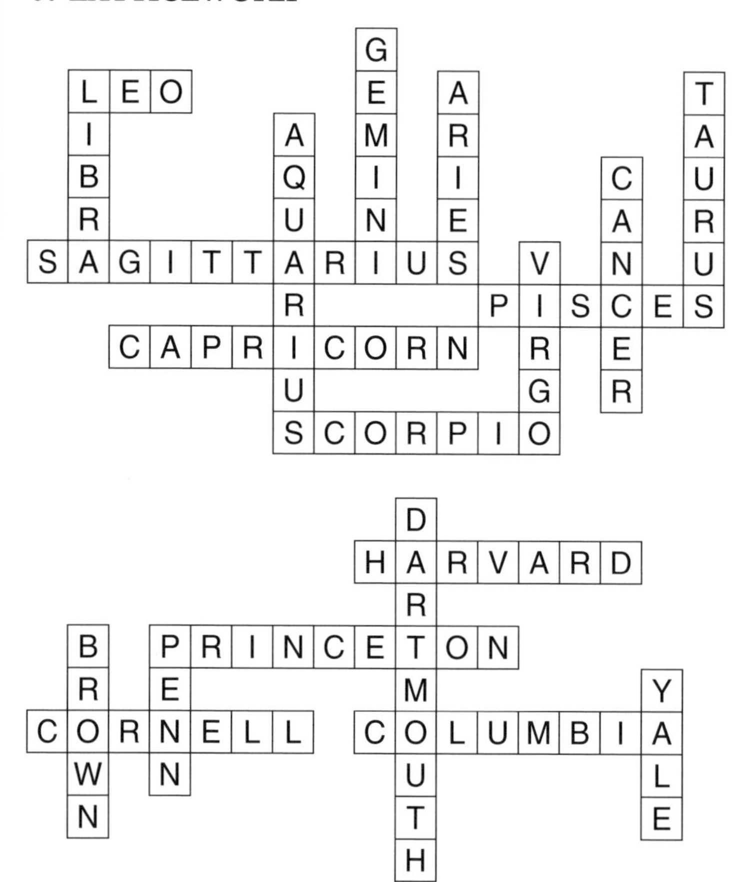

63 DOUBLE EXPOSURE

1 PLAY IT AGAIN, SAM; HAIL TO THE CHIEF
ZEPHYR, SALIVA, EATING, EYELID, QUILTS, THRONG, AGHAST, FIGHTS, AVENGE, PICNIC, KNIGHT, SWAMIS, CAVEAT, MYSELF

2 BELIEVE IT OR NOT; ADD AND SUBTRACT
ZEBRAS, KNEADS, PLEDGE, TRIVIA, REIGNS, REVVED, SEXISM, VIRTUE, TOMBOY, ORNATE, RAZORS, ENCAGE, TROPIC, TACTIC

41 SPLIT DECISIONS

67 SPLIT DECISIONS

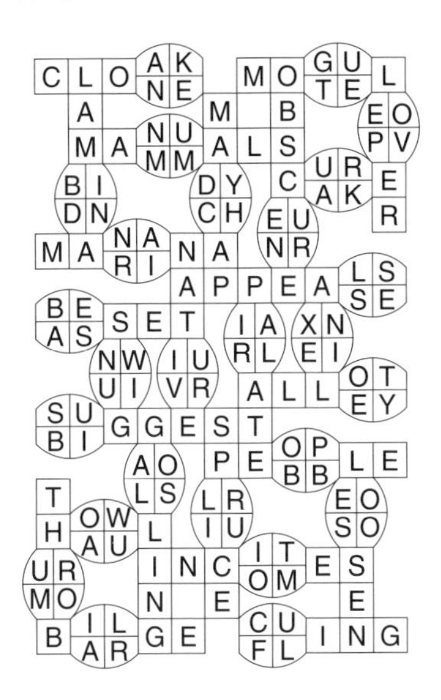

27 SPLIT DECISIONS

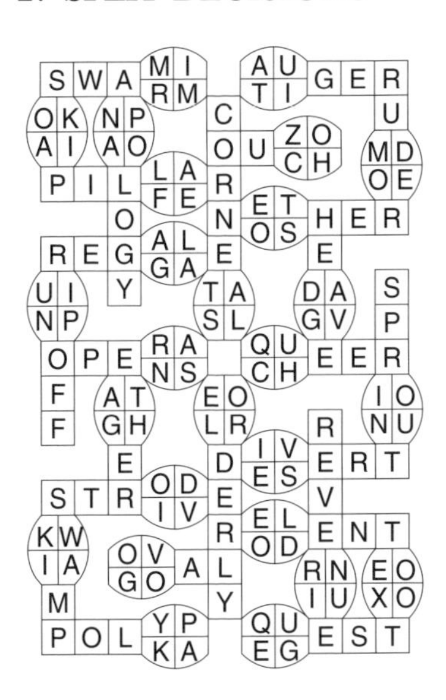

36 TRIAD SPLIT

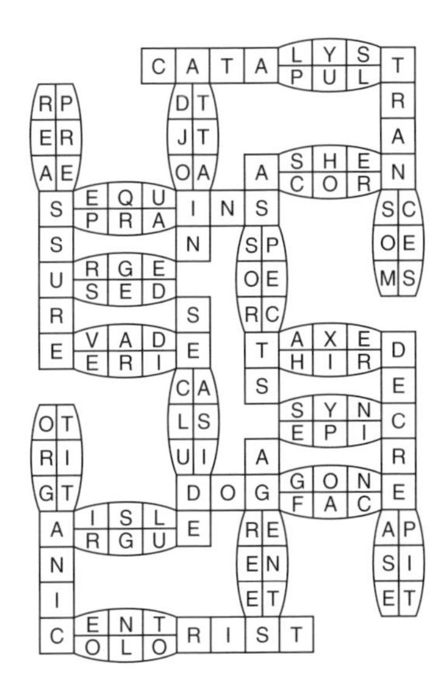

17 TWO BY TWO

23 FRAZE-IT

1 LASSOED; MINUS
2 MICE; CHILD
3 OPERA; FIDDLE
SODIUM CHLORIDE

1 SPECIAL; FRONT
2 FLOOD; PAL
3 QUARTET; ERROR
SEAFOOD PLATTER

13 MIXAGRAMS

KITTY + LOCO
ITCHY + ROOF
TOPIC + HERO
ENSUE + LADY
KITE CORD

GROAN + BIBS
OCCUR + BOOT
LIMIT + SODA
DENSE + DOUR
GOLD STAR

12 SPLIT DECISIONS

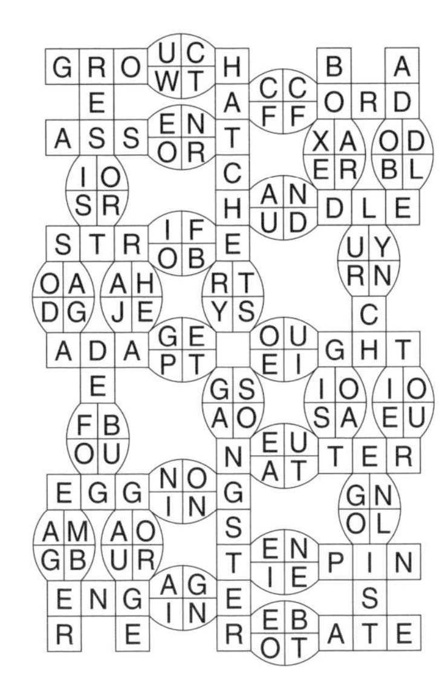

69 SPLIT DECISIONS

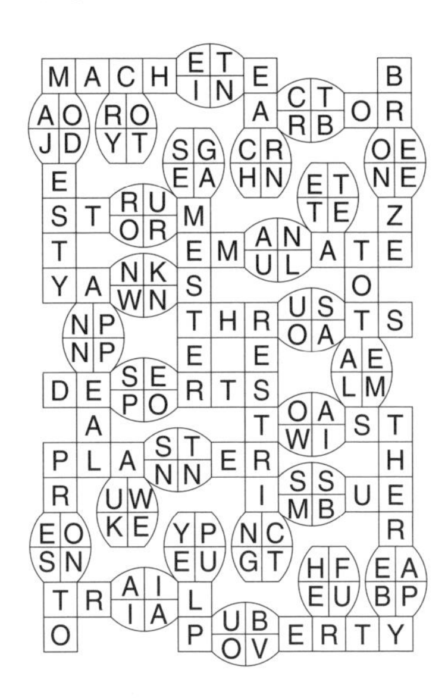

48 TRIAD SPLIT

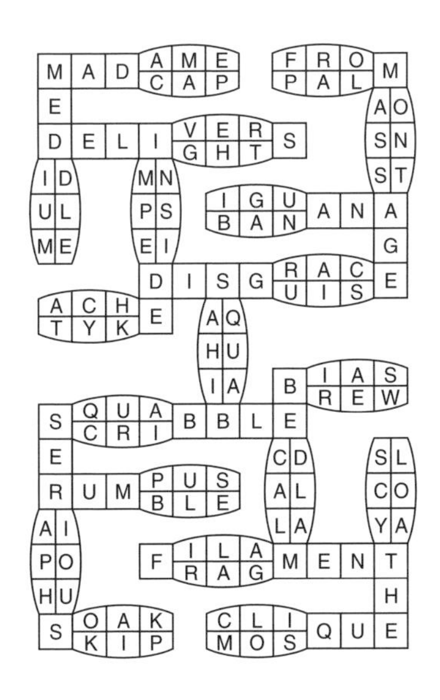

66 TRIAD SPLIT

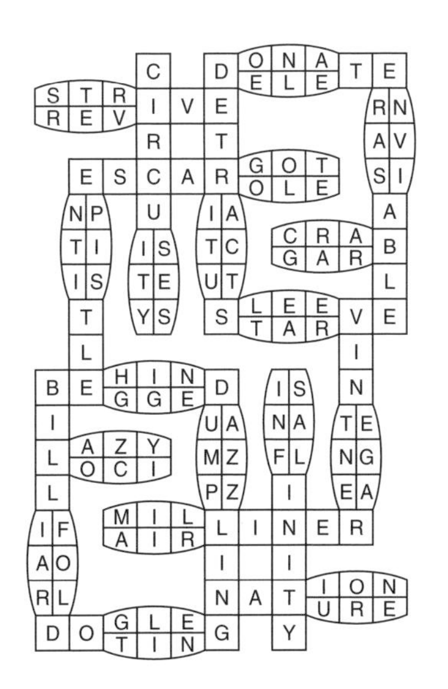

10 TWO BY TWO

D
E
E F E U D
D E A D E
I D I
F E E D F
I I
E E
D E F I E D

P
P O W W O W
P A W O P E
P E E W E E
A P
W I P E

B
B O O Z E
Z E B U Z
B Z O O
B I Z

21 SPLIT DECISIONS

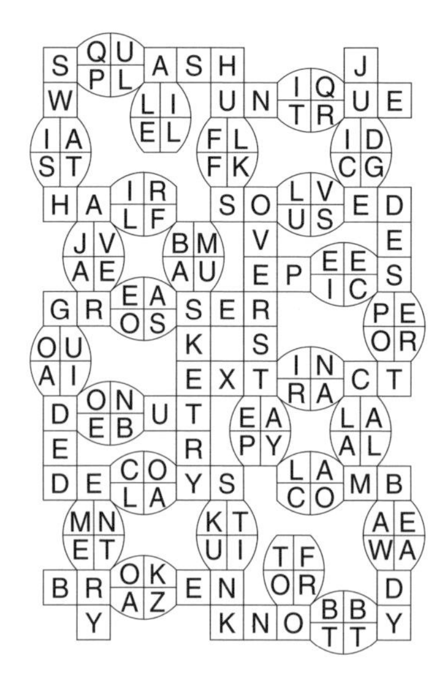

51 MIXAGRAMS

UNDID + WORN
DIODE + AVOW
ABODE + YOWL
CIRCA + SAKE
DOOR WAYS

NASAL + DEBT
APPAL + SAGA
MELON + BERG
EXERT + HIPS
NAME TAGS

70 SPLIT DECISIONS

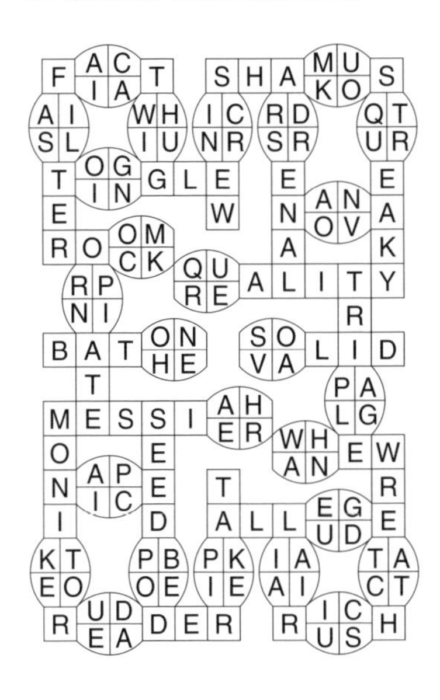

39 MIXAGRAMS

ASTER + EVEN
RISEN + SING
ADAPT + MEMO
FEMUR + AWED
SIDE VIEW

QUADS + SLID
GUARD + OMEN
VALUE + LEIS
BALMY + OOPS
DRUM SOLO

59 TWO BY TWO

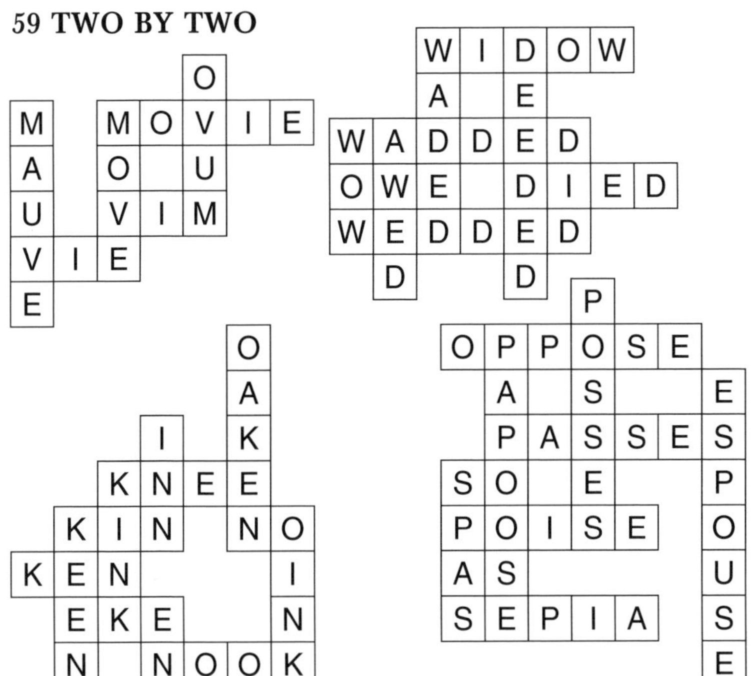

INDEX

ABOUT THE AUTHOR

GEORGE BREDEHORN is a retired teacher who lives in Wantagh, New York, with his wife Dorothy. He is the author of *Split Decisions & Other Word Puzzles* and *Ingenious Puzzles for Word Lovers*, both published by Sterling. He has invented more than 80 word games.

WHAT IS MENSA?

Mensa
The High IQ Society

Mensa is the international society for people with a high IQ. We have more than 100,000 members in over 40 countries worldwide.

The society's aims are:
- to identify and foster human intelligence for the benefit of humanity;
- to encourage research in the nature, characteristics, and uses of intelligence;
- to provide a stimulating intellectual and social environment for its members.

Anyone with an IQ score in the top two percent of the population is eligible to become a member of Mensa—are you the "one in 50" we've been looking for?

Mensa membership offers an excellent range of benefits:
- Networking and social activities nationally and around the world;
- Special Interest Groups (hundreds of chances to pursue your hobbies and interests—from art to zoology!);
- Monthly International Journal, national magazines, and regional newsletters;

- Local meetings—from game challenges to food and drink;
- National and international weekend gatherings and conferences;
- Intellectually stimulating lectures and seminars;
- Access to the worldwide SIGHT network for travelers and hosts.

For more information about Mensa International:
www.mensa.org
Mensa International
15 The Ivories
6–8 Northampton Street
Islington, London N1 2HY
United Kingdom

For more information about American Mensa:
www.us.mensa.org
Telephone: 1-800-66MENSA
American Mensa Ltd.
1229 Corporate Drive West
Arlington, TX 76006-6103 USA

For more information about British Mensa (UK and Ireland):
www.mensa.org.uk
Telephone: +44 (0) 1902 772771
E-mail: enquiries@mensa.org.uk
British Mensa Ltd.
St. John's House
St. John's Square
Wolverhampton WV2 4AH
United Kingdom

For more information about Australian Mensa:
www.au.mensa.org
Telephone: +61 1902 260 594
E-mail: info@au.mensa.org
Australian Mensa Inc.
PO Box 212
Darlington WA 6070 Australia